THE MACMILLAN BOOK OF
CHRISTMAS

To Eki and Rafe,
love Diz

THE MACMILLAN BOOK OF
CHRISTMAS

Illustrated by
Diz Wallis

Edited by
Alison Green

TED SMART

First published in 1999 by Macmillan Children's Books

This edition produced 1999 for The Book People Ltd,
Hall Wood Avenue, Haydock, St Helens, WA11 9UL.

ISBN 0 333 76606 7

1 3 5 7 9 8 6 4 2

A CIP catalogue record for this book is available from the British Library

Colour reproduction by Speedscan Ltd

Printed in Italy

Contents

Deck the Hall with Boughs of Holly
Christmas Preparations

Away in a Manger
The Christmas Story

$\mathcal{N}$ow Bring Us Some Figgy Pudding
Christmas Celebrations

$\mathcal{L}$ittle Donkey
Christmas Animals

A Partridge in a Pear Tree
Christmas Presents

Sir Winter
Christmas Weather

For Auld Lang Syne!
The New Year

$\mathcal{D}$eck the Hall
with Boughs of Holly

Christmas Preparations

Mr Willowby's Christmas Tree

Mr Willowby's Christmas tree
Came by special delivery.
Full and fresh and glistening green—
The biggest tree he had ever seen.

He dashed downstairs to open the door—
This was the moment he'd waited for.
"A magnificent tree! Splendid!" he cried.
"Please, sir, won't you carry it right inside.

"I think it might look best this year
Right in the parlour corner here."

But once the tree stood in its place,
Mr Willowby made a terrible face.
The tree touched the ceiling, then bent like a bow.
"Oh good heavens," he gasped. "Something must go!"

Baxter, the butler, was called on in haste,
To chop off the top, though it seemed quite a waste.
    "That's great," Mr Willowby cried with glee;
    "Now we can start to trim my tree."

When the trimming was well under way,
        The top was placed on a silver tray.
        Baxter said, "I know just who'd be
        Delighted with this Christmas tree."

        So it was presented to Miss Adelaide,
        Mr Willowby's upstairs maid.

    "Won't this tree be a pretty sight
        When I have trimmed it later tonight?
        But the top, oh dear, I'm so afraid,
    Will have to be cut," sighed Miss Adelaide.

    And so with scissors sharp and long
        She snipped off the top while she hummed a song.
        The top was set out the very next day
In the back of the house to be thrown away.

        That little treetop caught the eye
        Of Tim, the gardener, passing by.
        He certainly was not about
        To see that little tree thrown out.

He hurried it right home straightaway
To see what Mrs Tim would say.
"Fa la la . . . Surprise! Surprise!"
His wife could not believe her eyes.

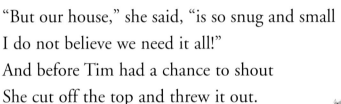

"But our house," she said, "is so snug and small
I do not believe we need it all!"
And before Tim had a chance to shout
She cut off the top and threw it out.

Barnaby Bear was padding by—
It almost hit him in the eye.
"Now who would throw a tree away
So very close to Christmas Day?

"I'll take it home, that's what I'll do!
Look, Mama Bear, I've a present for you."

"Isn't it a pretty tree,"
Yawned Mama Bear quite drowsily.
"Before we go to sleep this year
Let's have a Christmas party, dear."

But Little Bear, standing off far,
Cried out, "That tree won't hold a star!"
Barnaby said, "Let's cut a hunk
Off at the bottom, here at the trunk."

But Mama Bear just shook her head,
And sliced the treetop off instead.

"Jolly, by golly!" Barnaby said with a kick.
"Mama, that surely is just the right trick.
Let's trim it with bells and honey rings,
Some berries, and tinsel, and popcorn on strings."

Mama said, "Trim it just as you like,
I've got to tidy up for the night.
This top we won't need any more;
I'll put it just outside the door."

Later on that frosty night,
Frisky Fox came into sight.
He spied the treetop, rubbed his chin,
Opened his sack and stuffed the top in.

He scampered home and jumped his gate—
This Christmas present couldn't wait.
"It's even better than mincemeat pie,"
Said Mrs Fox with a happy sigh.

Then the Foxes saw that their Christmas prize
Was just a wee bit oversize.
"There, my dears, now don't you worry.
I'll fix this top now in a hurry."

Benjamin Rabbit found it then
Just outside the Foxes' den.
"It seems," he thought, "most certainly,
Santa left that for my family.

"Look," he cried, "see the tree I found!"
With that he called his family round.

Then there was a merrymaking,
Rollicking, frolicking, carrot-shaking
Celebration around the tree.
All were happy as rabbits can be.

Benjamin Rabbit, with his own hand,
Sliced a carrot and made a stand.
"Now let's see how this will look
In our little chimney nook."

But right away, the children cried,
"Look, it's leaning off to one side!"

"It's too tall, that's all," said Mrs Rabbit,
And as though it were a summer carrot,
 She gave it a chop
  And threw away . . . the top!

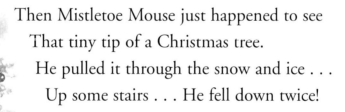

    Then Mistletoe Mouse just happened to see
        That tiny tip of a Christmas tree.
          He pulled it through the snow and ice . . .
            Up some stairs . . . He fell down twice!

        At last he reached his cosy house.
        "It's just the right size!" said Mrs Mouse.
            Then at the top, if you please,
        They put a star made out of cheese.

    Oh, wasn't it grand to have a tree—
    Exactly like Mr Willowby?

                        Robert Barry

They're Fetching in Ivy and Holly

"They're fetching in ivy and holly
And putting it this way and that.
I simply can't think of the reason,"
Said Si-Si the Siamese cat.

"They're pinning up lanterns and streamers.
There's mistletoe over the door.
They've brought in a tree from the garden.
I do wish I knew what it's for.

"It's covered with little glass candles
That go on and off without stop.
They've put it to stand in a corner
And tied up a fairy on top.

"They're stringing bright cards by the dozen
And letting them hang in a row.
Some people outside in the roadway
Are singing a song in the snow.

"I saw all the children write letters
And — I'm not at all sure this was wise —
They posted each one *up the chimney*.
I couldn't believe my own eyes.

"What on earth, in the middle of winter,
Does the family think it is at?
Won't somebody please come and tell me?"
Said Si-Si the Siamese cat.

Charles Causley

$\mathcal{A}$ Ghost Story
from "Memories of Christmas"

by Dylan Thomas

$\mathcal{B}$ring out the tall tales now that we told by the fire as we roasted chestnuts and the gaslight bubbled low. Ghosts with their heads under their arms trailed their chains and said whooo like owls in the long nights when I dared not look over my shoulder; wild beasts lurked in the cubbyhole under the stairs where the gas-meter ticked. "Once upon a time," Jim said, "there were some boys, just like us, who got lost in the dark in the snow, near Bethesda Chapel, and this is what happened to them . . ." It was the most dreadful happening I had ever heard.

And I remember that we went singing carols once, a night or two before Christmas Eve, when there wasn't the shaving of a moon to light the secret, white-flying streets. At the end of a long road was a drive that led to a large house, and we stumbled up the darkness of the drive that night,

each one of us afraid, each one holding a stone in his hand in case, and all of us too brave to say a word. The wind made through the drive-trees noises as of old and unpleasant and maybe webfooted men wheezing in caves. We reached the black bulk of the house. "What shall we give them?" Dan whispered. "Hark the Herald?" "Christmas Comes But Once A Year?" "No," Jack said, "we'll sing Good King Wenceslas. I'll count three." One, two, three, and we began to sing, our voices high and seemingly distant in the snow-felted darkness round the house that was occupied by nobody we knew. We stood close together, near the dark door.

> Good King Wenceslas looked out
> On the Feast of Stephen . . .

And then a small, dry voice, like the voice of someone who has not spoken for a long time, suddenly joined our singing: a small, dry voice from the other side of the door: a small dry voice through the keyhole.

And when we stopped running we were outside *our* house; the front room was lovely and bright; the gramophone was playing; we saw the red and white

balloons hanging from the gasmantle; uncles and aunts sat by the fire; I thought I smelt our supper being fried in the kitchen. Everything was good again, and Christmas shone through all the familiar town.

"Perhaps it was a ghost," Jim said, "Perhaps it was trolls," Dan said, who was always reading. "Let's go in and see if there's any jelly left," Jack said. And we did that.

Mince Pie Chant
A Christmas Counting Rhyme

Mince pies, mince pies,
going in to bake.

How many mince pies
did we make?

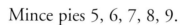

Mince pies 1, 2, 3 and 4.

Don't burn your fingers
on the hot oven door.

Mince pies 5, 6, 7, 8, 9.

Take 'em out. Try a bite.
Mmmmm! That's fine!

Tony Mitton

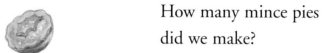

King John's Christmas

King John was not a good man—
    He had his little ways.
And sometimes no one spoke to him
    For days and days and days.
And men who came across him,
    When walking in the town,
Gave him a supercilious stare,
Or passed with noses in the air—
And bad King John stood dumbly there,
    Blushing beneath his crown.

King John was not a good man,
    And no good friends had he.
He stayed in every afternoon . . .
    But no one came to tea.
And, round about December,
    The cards upon his shelf
Which wished him lots of Christmas cheer,
And fortune in the coming year,
Were never from his near and dear,
    But only from himself.

King John was not a good man,
    Yet had his hopes and fears.
They'd given him no present now
    For years and years and years.
But every year at Christmas,
    While minstrels stood about,
Collecting tribute from the young
For all the songs they might have sung,
He stole away upstairs and hung
    A hopeful stocking out.

King John was not a good man,
    He lived his life aloof;
Alone he thought a message out
    While climbing up the roof.
He wrote it down and propped it
    Against the chimney stack:
"TO ALL AND SUNDRY—NEAR AND FAR—
F. CHRISTMAS IN PARTICULAR."
And signed it not "Johannes R."
    But very humbly, "JACK."

"I want some crackers,
    And I want some candy;
I think a box of chocolates
    Would come in handy;
I don't mind oranges,
    I do like nuts!
And I SHOULD like a pocket-knife
    That really cuts.
And, oh! Father Christmas, if you love me at all,
Bring me a big, red india-rubber ball!"

King John was not a good man—
    He wrote this message out,
And gat him to his room again,
    Descending by the spout.
And all that night he lay there,
    A prey to hopes and fears.
"I think that's him a-coming now."
(Anxiety bedewed his brow.)
"He'll bring one present, anyhow—
    The first I've had for years.

"Forget about the crackers,
      And forget about the candy;
I'm sure a box of chocolates
      Would never come in handy;
I don't like oranges,
      I don't want nuts,
And I HAVE got a pocket-knife
      That almost cuts.
But, oh! Father Christmas, if you love me at all,
Bring me a big, red india-rubber ball!"

King John was not a good man—
    Next morning when the sun
Rose up to tell a waiting world
    That Christmas had begun,
And people seized their stockings,
    And opened them with glee,
And crackers, toys and games appeared,
And lips with sticky sweets were smeared,
King John said grimly: "As I feared,
    Nothing again for me!

"I did want crackers,
    And I did want candy;
I know a box of chocolates
    Would come in handy;
I do love oranges,
    I did want nuts.
I haven't got a pocket-knife—
    Not one that cuts.
And, oh! if Father Christmas had loved me at all,
He would have brought a big, red india-rubber ball!"

King John stood by the window,
    And frowned to see below
The happy bands of boys and girls
    All playing in the snow.
A while he stood there watching,
    And envying them all . . .
When through the window big and red
There hurtled by his royal head,
And bounced and fell upon the bed,
    An india-rubber ball!

AND OH, FATHER CHRISTMAS
    MY BLESSINGS ON YOU FALL
        FOR BRINGING HIM
        A BIG, RED,
        INDIA-RUBBER
        BALL!

A. A. Milne

Deck the Hall

Deck the hall with boughs of holly,
   Fa la la la la, la la la la,
'Tis the season to be jolly,
   Fa la la la la, la la la la.
Don we now our gay apparel,
   Fa la la, la la la, la la la,
Sing the ancient Yule-tide carol,
   Fa la la la la, la la la la.

See the blazing Yule before us,
   Fa la la la la, la la la la,
Strike the harp and join the chorus,
   Fa la la la la, la la la la.
Follow me in merry measure,
   Fa la la, la la la, la la la,
While I tell of Yule-tide treasure,
   Fa la la la la, la la la la.

Fast away the old year passes,
Fa la la la la, la la la la,
Hail the new, you lads and lasses,
Fa la la la la, la la la la.
Sing we joyous all together,
Fa la la, la la la, la la la,
Heedless of the wind and weather,
Fa la la la la, la la la la.

Traditional

Christmas is Coming

Christmas is coming,
 The geese are getting fat,
Please to put a penny
 In the old man's hat.
If you haven't got a penny,
 A ha'penny will do;
If you haven't got a ha'penny,
 Then God bless you!

     Anon.

$\mathcal{M}$ole's Christmas

abridged from

The Wind in the Willows

by Kenneth Grahame

Mole didn't like spring cleaning. One spring, he decided he disliked it so much that he dashed out of his underground home and never went back. Instead, he spent a magical summer by the river with his new friend, Ratty, learning to row and to swim. Then, at Christmas, Mole and Rat were trudging back across country to the riverbank when, all of a sudden, Mole's nose picked up a familiar scent . . .

$\mathcal{H}$ome! That was what they meant, those caressing appeals, wafted through the air! Why, it must be quite close by him at that moment, his old home that he had hurriedly forsaken, that day when he first found the river! Since his escape on that bright morning he had hardly given it a thought. Now, with a rush of old memories, how clearly it stood up before him, in the darkness!

Shabby indeed, and small, and yet his, the home he had made for himself, the home he had been so happy to get back to after his day's work. And the home had been happy with him, too, and wanted him back, and was telling him so, through his nose.

"Ratty!" he called, full of joyful excitement, "hold on! Come back!"

"O, *come* along, Mole, do!" replied the Rat cheerfully, still plodding along.

"*Please* stop, Ratty!" pleaded the poor Mole. "You don't understand! It's my home, my old home! I've just come across the smell of it, and it's close by here, really quite close. And I *must* go to it, I must, I must!"

The Rat was by this time very far ahead, too far to hear clearly what the Mole was calling. And he was much taken up with the weather, for he too could smell something—something suspiciously like approaching snow.

"Mole, we mustn't stop now, really!" he called back. "It's late, and the snow's coming on again."

Poor Mole stood alone in the road, his heart torn asunder. But even under such a test as this his loyalty to his friend stood firm. Never for a moment did he dream of abandoning him. With a wrench that tore his very heartstrings he set his face down the road and followed submissively.

With an effort he caught up the unsuspecting Rat, who began chattering cheerfully about what they would do when they got back, and how jolly a fire of logs in the parlour would be, and what a supper he meant to eat; never noticing his companion's silence. At last, however, when they had gone some considerable way further, he stopped and said kindly, "Look here, Mole, old chap, you seem dead tired. We'll sit down here for a minute and rest. The snow has held off so far, and the best part of our journey is over."

The Mole subsided forlornly on a tree-stump. The sob he had fought with so long refused to be beaten. Up and up, it forced its way to the air,

and then another, and another, and others thick and fast; till poor Mole at last gave up the struggle, and cried freely and helplessly.

The Rat, astonished and dismayed, did not dare to speak for a while. At last he said, very quietly and sympathetically, "What is it, old fellow? Whatever can be the matter? Tell us your trouble, and let me see what I can do."

Poor Mole found it difficult to get any words out. "I know it's a—shabby, dingy little place," he sobbed forth at last, brokenly: "but it was my own little home —and I was fond of it—and then I smelt it suddenly—on the road, when I called and you wouldn't listen, Rat—and everything came back to me with a rush—and I *wanted* it!—O dear, O dear!—I thought my heart would break."

The Rat stared straight in front of him, saying nothing, only patting Mole gently on the shoulder. After a time he muttered, "I see it all now! What a *pig* I have been! A pig—that's me! A plain pig!"

He waited till Mole's sobs became gradually less stormy and more rhythmical. Then he rose from his seat, and, remarking carelessly, "Well, now we'd really better be getting on, old chap!" set off up the road again, over the toil-some way they had come.

"Wherever are you (hic) going to (hic), Ratty?" cried the tearful Mole, looking up in alarm.

"We're going to find that home of yours, old fellow," replied the Rat pleasantly; "so you had better come along, for it will take some finding, and we shall want your nose."

"O, come back, Ratty, do!" cried the Mole, getting up and hurrying after him. "It's no good, I tell you! It's too late, and too dark, and the place is too far off, and the snow's coming! And—and I never meant to let you know I was feeling that way about it! And think of River Bank, and your supper!"

"Hang River Bank, and supper too!" said the Rat heartily. "I tell you, I'm going to find this place now, if I stay out all night. So cheer up, old chap, and take my arm, and we'll very soon be back there again."

Still snuffling, pleading, and reluctant, Mole suffered himself to be dragged back along the road. When at last it seemed to the Rat that they must be nearing that part of the road where the Mole had been "held up", he said, "Now, use your nose, and give your mind to it."

They moved on in silence for some little way, when suddenly the Rat was conscious, through his arm that was linked in Mole's, of a faint sort of electric thrill that was passing down that animal's body.

The signals were coming through!

Mole stood a moment rigid, while his uplifted nose, quivering slightly, felt the air.

Then a short, quick run forward— a fault—a check—a try back; and then a slow, steady, confident advance.

The Rat, much excited, kept close to his heels as the Mole crossed a dry ditch,

scrambled through a hedge, and nosed his way over a field.

Suddenly, without giving warning, he dived; but the Rat was on the alert, and promptly followed him down the tunnel to which his unerring nose had faithfully led him.

It was close and airless, and the earthy smell was strong, and it seemed a long time to Rat ere the passage ended and he could stand erect and stretch and shake himself. The Mole struck a match, and by its light the Rat saw that they were standing in an open space, neatly swept and sanded underfoot, and directly facing them was Mole's little front door, with "Mole End" painted, in Gothic lettering, over the bell-pull at the side.

Mole reached down a lantern from a nail on the wall and lit it, and the Rat, looking round him, saw that they were in a sort of fore-court. A garden-seat stood on one side of the door, and on the other, a roller;

for the Mole, who was a tidy animal when at home, could not stand having his ground kicked up by other animals. In the middle was a small round pond containing goldfish and surrounded by a cockle-shell border.

Mole's face beamed at the sight of these objects so dear to him, and he hurried Rat through the door, lit a lamp in the hall, and took one glance round his old home. He saw the dust lying thick on everything, saw the cheerless, deserted look of the long-neglected house, its worn and shabby contents—and collapsed on a hall-chair, his nose in his paws. "O, Ratty!" he cried dismally, "Why ever did I do it? Why did I bring you to this poor, cold little place, on a night like this, when you might have been at River Bank by this time, toasting your toes before a blazing fire, with all your own nice things about you!"

The Rat paid no heed. He was running here and there, opening doors, inspecting rooms and cupboards, and lighting lamps and candles and sticking them up everywhere. "What a capital little house this is!" he called out cheerily "So compact! So well planned! Everything here and everything in its place! We'll make a jolly night of it. The first thing we want is a good fire; I'll see to that—I always know where to find things. You get a duster, Mole, and try and smarten things up a bit. Bustle about, old chap!"

Mole roused himself and dusted and polished with energy and heartiness, while the Rat, running to and fro with armfuls of fuel, soon had a cheerful blaze roaring up the chimney. He hailed the Mole to come

and warm himself; but Mole promptly had another fit of the blues.

"Rat," he moaned, "how about your supper, you poor, cold, hungry, weary animal? I've nothing to give you—nothing—not a crumb!"

"What a fellow you are for giving in!" said the Rat reproachfully. "Why, only just now I saw a sardine-opener on the kitchen dresser, and everybody knows that means there are sardines about somewhere. Rouse yourself! pull yourself together, and come with me and forage."

They went and foraged accordingly, hunting through every cupboard and turning out every drawer. The result was not so very depressing after all; a tin of sardines—a box of captain's biscuits, nearly full—and a German sausage encased in silver paper.

"There's a banquet for you!" observed the Rat, as he arranged the table.

"No bread!" groaned the Mole dolorously; "no butter, no—"

"No *pâté de foie gras*, no champagne!" continued the Rat, grinning. "This is really the jolliest little place I ever was in. No wonder you're so fond of it, Mole."

The Rat had just got seriously to work with the sardine-opener when sounds were heard from the fore-court without—sounds like the scuffling of small feet in the gravel and a confused murmur of tiny voices, while broken sentences reached them—"Now, all in a line—hold the

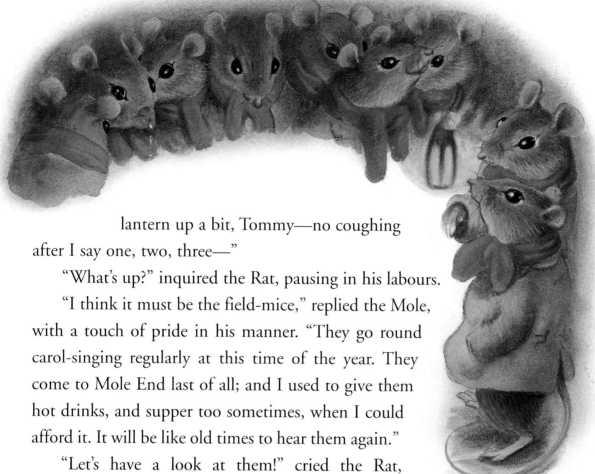

lantern up a bit, Tommy—no coughing
after I say one, two, three—"

"What's up?" inquired the Rat, pausing in his labours.

"I think it must be the field-mice," replied the Mole,
with a touch of pride in his manner. "They go round
carol-singing regularly at this time of the year. They
come to Mole End last of all; and I used to give them
hot drinks, and supper too sometimes, when I could
afford it. It will be like old times to hear them again."

"Let's have a look at them!" cried the Rat,
jumping up to the door.

It was a pretty sight, and a seasonable one, that met their eyes when
they flung the door open. In the fore-court, lit by the dim rays of a horn
lantern, some eight or ten little field-mice stood in a semi-circle, red
worsted comforters round their throats, their fore-paws thrust deep into
their pockets, their feet jigging for warmth. With bright beady eyes they
glanced shyly at each other, sniggering a little, sniffing and applying coat-
sleeves a good deal. As the door opened, one of the elder ones that carried
the lantern was just saying, "Now then, one, two, three!" and forthwith

their shrill little voices uprose on the air, singing one of the old-time carols that their forefathers composed:

Villagers all, this frosty tide,
Let your doors swing open wide,
Though wind may follow, and snow beside,
Yet draw us in by your fire to bide;
    Joy shall be yours in the morning!

Here we stand in the cold and the sleet,
Blowing fingers and stamping feet,
Come from far away you to greet—
You by fire and we in the street—
    Bidding you joy in the morning!

For ere one half of the night was gone,
Sudden a star has led us on,
Raining bliss and benison—
Bliss tomorrow and more anon,
    Joy for every morning!

Goodman Joseph toiled through the snow—
Saw the star o'er a stable low;
Mary she might not further go—
Welcome thatch, and litter below!
    Joy was hers in the morning!

And then they heard the angels tell
"Who were the first to cry Nowell?
Animals all, as it befell,
In the stable where they did dwell!
    Joy shall be theirs in the morning!"

The voices ceased, the singers, bashful but smiling, exchanged sidelong glances, and silence succeeded—but for a moment only.

"Very well sung, boys!" cried the Rat heartily. "And now come along in, all of you, and warm yourselves by the fire, and have something hot!"

"Yes come along, field-mice," cried the Mole eagerly. "This is quite like old times! Shut the door after you. Pull up that settle to the fire. Now, you just wait a minute, while we—O, Ratty!" he cried in despair. "Whatever are we doing? We've nothing to give them!"

"You leave all that to me," said the masterful Rat. "Here, you with the lantern! Come over this way. I want to talk to you. Now, tell me, are there any shops open at this hour of the night?"

"Why, certainly, sir," replied the field-mouse respectfully. "At this time of the year our shops keep open to all sorts of hours."

"Then look here!" said the Rat. "You go off at

once, you and your lantern, and you get me—"

Here much muttered conversation ensued. Finally, there was a chink of coins passing from paw to paw, the field-mouse was provided with an ample basket for his purchases, and off he hurried.

The rest of the field-mice, perched in a row on the settle, their small legs swinging, gave themselves up to the enjoyment of the fire, and toasted their chilblains till they tingled.

It was not long before the latch clicked, the door opened, and the field-mouse with the lantern reappeared, staggering under the weight of his basket.

Under the generalship of Rat, everybody was set to do something or to fetch something. In a very few minutes supper was ready, and Mole, as he took the head of the table in a sort of dream, saw his little friends' faces brighten and beam as they fell to without delay; and then let himself loose—for he was famished indeed—on the provender so magically provided, thinking what a happy home-coming this had turned out, after all.

Away in a Manger

The Christmas Story

Kings Came Riding

Kings came riding
    One, two and three,
Over the desert
    And over the sea.

One in a ship
    With a silver mast;
The fishermen wondered
    As he went past.

One on a horse
    With a saddle of gold;
The children came running
    To behold.

One came walking,
    Over the sand,
With a casket of treasure
    Held in his hand.

All the people
    Said, "Where go they?"
But the kings went forward
    All through the day.

Night came on
    As those kings went by;
They shone like the gleaming
    Stars in the sky.

Charles Williams

O Little Town of Bethlehem

O little town of Bethlehem,
How still we see thee lie!
Above thy deep and dreamless sleep
The silent stars go by:
Yet in thy dark streets shineth
The everlasting Light;
The hopes and fears of all the years
Are met in thee tonight.

O, morning stars, together
Proclaim the holy birth,
And praises sing to God the King
And peace to men on earth.
For Christ is born of Mary;
And, gathered all above,
While mortals sleep, the angels keep
Their watch of wondering love.

How silently, how silently,
The wondrous gift is given!
So God imparts to human hearts
The blessings of His heaven.
No ear may hear His coming;
But in this world of sin,
Where meek souls will receive Him, still
The dear Christ enters in.

O holy Child of Bethlehem,
Descend to us, we pray;
Cast out our sins, and enter in:
Be born in us today.
We hear the Christmas angels
The great glad tidings tell:
O come to us, abide with us,
Our Lord Emmanuel.

Bishop Phillips Brooks

The Story of the Nativity

The Birth of Jesus

from The Gospel According to St Luke,
Chapter 2, verses 1–7

And it came to pass in those days, that there went out a decree from Caesar Augustus, that all the world should be taxed . . . And all went to be taxed, every one into his own city. And Joseph also went up from Galilee, out of the city of Nazareth, into Judea, unto the city of David, which is called Bethlehem (because he was of the house and lineage of David) to be taxed with Mary his espoused wife, being great with child.

And so it was, that, while they were there, the days were accomplished that she should be delivered. And she brought forth her first-born son, and wrapped him in swaddling clothes, and laid him in a manger, because there was no room for them in the inn.

The Shepherds' Story

from The Gospel According to St Luke,
Chapter 2, verses 8–20

And there were in the same country shepherds abiding in the field, keeping watch over their flock by night. And, lo, the angel of the Lord came upon them, and the glory of the Lord shone round about them, and they were sore afraid. And the angel said unto them, "Fear not: for, behold, I bring you good tidings of great joy, which shall be to all people. For unto you is born this day in the city of David a Saviour, which is Christ the Lord. And this shall be a sign unto you: ye shall find the babe wrapped in swaddling clothes, lying in a manger."

And suddenly there was with the angel a multitude of the heavenly host praising God, and saying, "Glory to God in the highest, and on earth peace, good will toward men."

And it came to pass, as the angels were gone away from them into heaven, the shepherds said one to another, "Let us now go even unto Bethlehem, and see this thing which is come to pass, which the Lord hath made known unto us." And they came with haste, and found Mary, and Joseph, and the babe lying in a manger. And when they had seen it, they made known abroad the saying which was told them concerning this child. And all they that heard it wondered at those things which were told them by the shepherds.

But Mary kept all these things, and pondered them in her heart. And the shepherds returned, glorifying and praising God for all the things that they had heard and seen, as it was told unto them.

The Wise Men's Story

from The Gospel According to St Matthew,
Chapter 2, verses 1–14

Now when Jesus was born in Bethlehem of Judea in the days of Herod the king, behold, there came wise men from the east to Jerusalem, saying, "Where is he that is born King of the Jews? For we have seen his star in the east, and are come to worship him."

When Herod the king had heard these things, he was troubled, and all Jerusalem with him. And when he had gathered all the chief priests and scribes of the people together, he demanded of them where Christ should be born. And they said unto him, "In Bethlehem of Judea: for thus it is written by the prophet, 'And thou Bethlehem, in the land of Juda, art not the least among the princes of Juda: for out of thee shall come a Governor, that shall rule my people Israel.'"

Then Herod, when he had privily called the wise men, inquired of them diligently what time the star appeared. And he sent them to Bethlehem, and said, "Go and search diligently for the young child; and when ye have found him, bring me word again, that I may come and worship him also."

When they had heard the king, they departed; and, lo, the star, which they saw in the east, went before them, till it came and stood over where the young child was.

When they saw the star, they rejoiced with exceeding great joy. And when they were come into the house, they saw the young child with Mary his mother, and fell down, and worshipped him; and when they had opened their treasures, they presented unto him gifts; gold, and frankincense, and myrrh.

And being warned of God in a dream that they should not return to Herod, they departed into their own country another way. And when they were departed, behold, the angel of the Lord appeareth to Joseph in a dream, saying, "Arise, and take the young child and his mother, and flee into Egypt, and be thou there until I bring thee word: for Herod will seek the young child to destroy him."

When he arose, he took the young child and his mother by night, and departed into Egypt.

High in the Heaven

High in the Heaven
A gold star burns
Lighting our way
As the great world turns.

Silver the frost
It shines on the stem.
As we now journey
To Bethlehem.

White is the ice
At our feet as we tread,
Pointing a path
To the manger-bed.

Charles Causley

The Holly and the Ivy

The holly and the ivy,
When they are both full grown,
Of all the trees that are in the wood,
The holly bears the crown.

The rising of the sun
And the running of the deer,
The playing of the merry organ,
Sweet singing in the choir.

The holly bears a blossom,
As white as the lily flower,
And Mary bore sweet Jesus Christ
To be our sweet Saviour.

The holly bears a berry,
As red as any blood,
And Mary bore sweet Jesus Christ
To do poor sinners good.

The holly bears a prickle,
As sharp as any thorn,
And Mary bore sweet Jesus Christ
On Christmas day in the morn.

The holly bears a bark,
As bitter as any gall,
And Mary bore sweet Jesus Christ
For to redeem us all.

The holly and the ivy,
When they are both full grown,
Of all the trees that are in the wood,
The holly bears the crown.

Traditional

Away in a Manger

Away in a manger, no crib for a bed,
The little Lord Jesus laid down His sweet head.
The stars in the bright sky looked down
　　where He lay,
The little Lord Jesus asleep on the hay.

The cattle are lowing, the Baby awakes,
But little Lord Jesus, no crying He makes.
I love thee, Lord Jesus, look down
　　from the sky,
And stay by my side until morning is nigh.

Be near me, Lord Jesus; I ask Thee to stay
Close by me for ever, and love me, I pray.
Bless all the dear children in Thy tender care,
And fit us for heaven to live with Thee there.

Traditional

The Witness

by Robert Westall

A great wind blew out of Asia; from that finger of ice that would one day be called Everest. It thundered across white Steppes, and disturbed the King of Parthia's slumbers. Cyrenius, Governor of Syria, tossed and turned, worrying about the Egyptian furniture, shipped to Rome three days before.

Across the desert the wind blew icy and dry. But when it reached the warmth of Jordan it dropped flurries of snow. One of them caught the cat as she reached the crest of the stable roof. She crouched wretched; the wind blowing her fur into wild saucers, exposing points of warm, pink, vulnerable skin. She spat into the wind's face in helpless fury.

Her misery was total. She was heavy with kitten. In this, her first year of exile, she was unprepared for the Judean cold. Worse, she couldn't find a dark private place to give birth. Turned out of cellar and byre by servants putting down straw and blankets for extra guests. Strangers everywhere.

Egypt had been so different: basking in the sun on the temple terrace; dabbling for fish in the green waters of the temple canal; the manicured hands of the priests, who thought it a prayer to stroke her. The common people would hold back the carts while she stepped past. In Egypt, she was a goddess, the spirit of Bastet-Ra, Mother of the Sacred Trinity, cat-goddess of Bubastis by the Nile. Parents would sell the hair of their children to bring her offerings, watch with bated breath as she washed, counting the number of times her paw crossed her ear, believing that this foretold the future.

This stable was her last hope. Leaking roof, flaking mud walls that let in draughts, old straw full of the smells of other animals. But better than nothing. If she gave birth in the open, the wind would kill the kittens before morning.

She leapt to the ground, with a sickening grunt. Yet even in her wretchedness she was graceful. Golden, long-legged, huge-eared.

In the doorway, she spat again. People even here; poor people too, from the smell. Rich strangers were sometimes well enough. Their perfumes reminded her of the temple. They might stroke her, feed her from their own rich food bowls; but poor people drove her out with shouts and blows . . .

She still couldn't understand why her world had changed. One morning she had been lured from the temple by the breeze from the quayside. Lost in a dream of fish, she had met a bearded stranger in the alley. She had paused, one foot uplifted, waiting for him to step aside. Instead, rough hands seized her and thrust her into the sudden darkness of a sack. Such outrage! Then such endless blind jogging! Such sickness, such hunger, thirst and the unbearable smell of her own filth! Such useless gnawing and clawing to escape!

Finally, rough guttural voices and the chink of coins.

"Sure she's good at killing rats?"

"Good? She's the reason there's always corn in Egypt. Have you never seen the Egyptians' granaries? How d'you think they keep rats out? These creatures are such ratters the Egyptians worship them."

The other man made a noise of disgust, deep in his throat.

"You are asking me to take a devil of Gehenna into my house!"

"Better a devil than rats, brother. The price of this particular devil is still seven denarii. If the Egyptians had found her in my baggage they would have slain me."

Her sack was rudely thrust into ruder

hands. The neck was pulled open, and she was tipped onto a mud floor so hard it hurt her paws. Then a door slammed and she was in the dark again. She sat down and washed her shoulder to calm herself. Suddenly a rustling among the straw made her ears prick. At least she would not go hungry.

When she had killed and fed, she found a hole in the wall and rapidly enlarged it. Outside, in an utterly strange blurred landscape, and a thousand smells, all alien, she crouched to relieve herself. She was free; but all roads were the same, and none gave even a whiff of Bubastis, no matter how much she widened her nostrils to the breeze. From that day, her prison became her safe place and hunting ground. Her new owner, picking over the remains of her kills, was well enough pleased, and ignored her.

Others were less kind. When she descended to the ground men cursed and kicked her, and children threw stones; so she learned to keep to the rooftops and the night. But when the weight grew in her belly, and the flurry of kicking inside warned her that the time had come to find a safer place still, she knew she must not stay in that barn . . .

She had turned away from the
stable door when an even crueller blast of wind
caught her, at the same time as the first contraction in her belly. Making
the bitterest of choices, she turned again, and slipped inside. It was dark,
but to her eyes clear as crystal. Near the door a plough-ox chewed the cud
lazily, lying half on its side. The straw where it lay was thick and clean, but
no good for a nest. The creature might roll, crushing mother and kitten
altogether in the moment of birth . . .

Further in a grey donkey stamped. A striped blanket had been thrown
over its back, and a man fussed around it with furrowed brow and a cross,
anxious voice. His breath and the donkey's steamed together in the frosty
air. Further in still, a woman lay, on straw not so thick and clean as the
ox's bed. A lamp gave her light, and enough warmth to hold her hands out
to. And there was a patch of shadow in the corner behind. The cat crept
forward, silently, sagging belly pressed close to the floor.

But the man saw her, shouted. Reached for a long stick. He blocked
her retreat. She leapt into the shadowed corner, back arched and teeth
bared. The man advanced, but the woman put up her hand.

"Nay. Have mercy. She is in the same plight as myself. Are we so
poor we can't share what we have?"

"Dirty things . . . if the child should be born tonight . . . they lie on children's faces and steal their breath . . ."

"Nay. She will soon have enough to keep her busy. And see, she is clean. She is the cleanest thing in this poor place." The man turned, spreading his hands.

"I'm sorry! I *always* stay with my father's cousin when I come here. He must have known I was coming for the census. So why is his house full of strangers? I will tell you why. Because strangers have money. It is the Romans' fault; they destroy the old ways . . ."

"Husband, husband. Calm yourself. You are not to blame for your father's cousin. I shall do well enough here." The man grunted, soothed. "But let the little cat stay. She will keep me company. All women find this waiting dreary. See, she's snuggling in."

And, certainly, the cat's fear seemed quite gone. She crouched against the woman's robe, kneading furiously with her forepaws.

The cat could not understand it. She could still feel the draughts catching at her fur, yet she was deliciously warm. The spiky straw seemed as soft as a silken temple cushion. And though the lamp guttered, the room seemed bathed in golden light, brighter than the sun on the temple of Bastet-Ra. She slowly crept up the robe, till her nose rested against the woman's neck. But the woman formed a nest in the straw of the dark corner, and put the cat into it; and there presently two kittens were born. Two only, for the winter-gods had

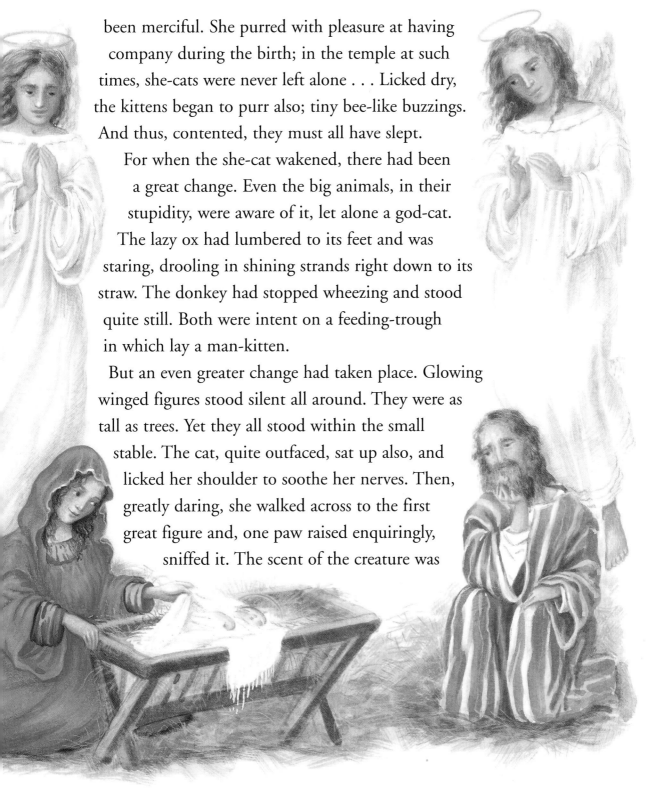

been merciful. She purred with pleasure at having
company during the birth; in the temple at such
times, she-cats were never left alone . . . Licked dry,
the kittens began to purr also; tiny bee-like buzzings.
And thus, contented, they must all have slept.

For when the she-cat wakened, there had been
a great change. Even the big animals, in their
stupidity, were aware of it, let alone a god-cat.
The lazy ox had lumbered to its feet and was
staring, drooling in shining strands right down to its
straw. The donkey had stopped wheezing and stood
quite still. Both were intent on a feeding-trough
in which lay a man-kitten.

But an even greater change had taken place. Glowing
winged figures stood silent all around. They were as
tall as trees. Yet they all stood within the small
stable. The cat, quite outfaced, sat up also, and
licked her shoulder to soothe her nerves. Then,
greatly daring, she walked across to the first
great figure and, one paw raised enquiringly,
sniffed it. The scent of the creature was

overpoweringly beautiful; better even than the lotus-flower in summer. She went on to the next, and the next. Each smelt differently, but all Heavenly.

Among the winged figures came a ripple of mirth.

"The cat sees us. Even the ox and ass. Why cannot the man?"

For the man was walking up and down, frowning thunderously.

"Are you sure you're all right? Is the child well? I would be happier if the midwife came to look at you . . ." He walked straight through one of the great winged figures. The cat, watching, arched her back in alarm. But nothing happened, except another ripple of mirth among the winged creatures.

"Husband, we have no need of a midwife. It was an easy birth. How could it have been otherwise?"

The man grunted, deep in his throat. "Oh, I know, I know."

"Cannot you even feel those who guard us? The little cat can *see* them!"

Just then, the Child opened His eyes. The golden light that had been in the stable was as nothing to that which was suddenly there. The glowing beings covered their faces with their wings. But the she-cat inched towards him, as if drawn by a magnet.

"Look out, Mary, the cat!"

But the furry body stopped short, feet folded beneath her and green eyes blinking as she might have blinked at a fire. And such a storm of purring as threatened to shake her apart. The woman said, "Let her worship also."

The cat dozed again, till the door banged back and the frosty wind blew in. Five men stood there, in greasy sheepskins. Their eyes seemed to fill their faces, and their mouths were permanently open. Having shut the door, they shuffled uneasily.

"This be un place. See, there's babe in feeding-trough. And more o' they bright-shining fellers. Beggin' yer pardon, gaffer." They all bobbed to the nearest winged creature.

The woman's husband came forward. "What are you jabbering about? You can't come in here. We're packed out already."

"But the shining feller spoke to us. Told us we were to come, and what we'd find. And here it be, just like he said . . ."

And without another word, they knelt to the Child. The cat shifted uneasily but held her station, even when the newborn lamb bleated loudly, leapt from a shepherd's arms, and ran straight into the oil lamp, nearly setting the straw alight. Stupid creature, thought the cat. But then lambs were not reared in temples . . .

The shepherds left in the end, persuaded to take their noisy lamb. "It needs its mother," said the woman.

The Child slept again, and the great light dimmed, but did not depart. The man sat in the doorway, as if on guard, but soon he pulled his robe up around his ears, his head dropped, and he slept the racking, snoring sleep of exhaustion.

The woman closed her eyes, but did not sleep. The smile stayed on her face, even when she eased her aching body on the straw. The cat lay, desiring never to move from this place again.

But in the far corner, something rustled in the straw. The cat's ears pricked. She turned.

A rat was coming towards the Child. It moved slowly on its belly, as if dazed. Its little red eyes shone.

Outrage filled the cat. The worst thing in her world was approaching the best. She wriggled her lean bottom and pounced. The rat squealed once as she bit into its neck. The man and woman came to, with a start. Then they saw what had happened. "See, she guards the Child," said the woman sleepily.

"They have their uses," grudged the man, and dozed again. The taste of rat's blood in her mouth made the cat feel ravenous.

But, far more important, she now had a gift to bring the man-kitten. She crept nearer, dragging the limp body. The Child opened His blue eyes, and the cat laid the rat by Him.

But there was no praise or pleasure for her. The Child's grief over the rat broke over her like a storm, till she hunched her body, laid back her ears, and whimpered in pain.

The Child tossed restlessly, flung out one tiny arm towards the rat. The creature's poor death-flattened belly gave one frantic heave, its eyes opened and shone red and bright. Slowly it dragged itself to its feet and inspected itself with a bewildered twitching nose.

Then side by side, cat and rat watched, until the cock crowed.

By the time the rich men came, the kittens had their ears half-pricked and their eyes wide open, and they were driving the she-cat frantic with their wobble-legged journeys through the straw. When the Child heard them draw near, He would give a gurgle of delight. The  kittens were well-fed, sleek like their mother. But not with the killing of rats, not ever. There was no need; now there were always scraps in plenty.

When the rich men had presented their gifts, and were sitting at ease with the mother, they noticed the cat.

"So the star has led others here before us?"

"How so?" asked the woman.

"Even the gods of Egypt come to worship. This is a sacred cat from Bubastis' temple on the Nile. When did they bring her? She is a gift greater than ours."

"She arrived on her own, in the very hour of the Child's birth."

"Incredible," said Melchior.

"Unbelievable," said Caspar.

"Egypt knows the stars," said fierce-moustached Balthasar.

"What manner of god is this Bastet-Ra?" asked the woman, curious. "Does she demand blood-sacrifice?"

"Nay," said Melchior. "She is a gentle god, a country-people's god. She brings fertile harvests. Maidens pray to her for a husband, and married women for an easy childbirth. Her worship is through dances and merriment and the right mothering of children. Egypt is a kindly place, under her rule."

"She is a demon," said Joseph. Recent events had mellowed him a little, but not much.

"Nay, husband, be not so narrow. Good is always good. These good men are not of our ways either, but they have come so far to be here. Tell me, Melchior, of the place this little one came from."

So Melchior spoke of the broad-bosomed Nile, and the yearly flood that brought fat crops, so that none starved. And the people going down the river to Bubastis, singing and dancing on the brown-winged ships.

"Poor little one," said the woman, stroking the cat's fur. "How you must miss the sun."

The rich men had gone. They had talked of Herod; and when they talked of Herod, they lowered the lids of their shrewd eyes, and shook their heads. Something worried their subtle minds. When they left, they didn't go back to Jerusalem, though that would have been their easiest way.

There was always peace in the stable; but less than usual that night. The man tossed and groaned in his sleep. Suddenly, he awakened with a frightened shout.

"What ails you, husband?"

"I have seen an angel of the Lord."

"Thanks be to God He has taken away your blindness."

"You do not understand. It was the Dark Angel: the Angel of Death."

Clinging together, they turned to look at the sleeping Child.

"What are we to do? Were you not told?"

The man laughed harshly.

"I was told to do one thing, that I should have done days ago. I was told to take that devil back to its owner." He threw a stick at the cat, which missed. The cat withdrew into a corner, calling the kittens to her urgently.

"But we do not know the owner . . ."

"*I* do—I have asked around. Aaron bar Joshua. A godless man who bought her from a Syrian camel driver . . ."

"But how will that help us?"

The man gave a laugh as short as a curse.

"The angel forgot to mention that."

The woman said thoughtfully, "Aaron bar Joshua is *not* the owner. He bought her from a thief. Her real owner dwells in the land of Egypt . . ."

"Woman, we cannot go to Egypt. How would we live? They are expecting us back at Nazareth. We have tarried *here* too long . . ."

"Would you disobey an angel, Joseph? Even *that* angel?"

In spite of the great danger, there was a last ripple of mirth among the great winged figures; their light was dimmer, now, but the cat could still sense them.

"We shall take this little one home," said the woman, in a voice that was low but determined. "And we shall make a home there ourselves, until another angel comes."

And so, next morning, they packed hastily. And Joseph's father's cousin, repenting of his coldness (and having heard some talk of kings, gifts and a Messiah) found he could lend them all manner of things. And so they went from Bethlehem more comfortably than they had come. And on the donkey's back, twin kitten-heads poked from among the baggage.

And as each dawn turned the sky pink over the distant lands of Egypt, a swift long-legged streak ran before them, across the flat plains of Sinai.

The cat of Bastet-Ra was going home.

Silent Night

Silent night! Holy night!
All is calm, all is bright;
Round the Virgin Mother and Child,
Holy infant so tender and mild,
Sleep in heavenly peace,
Sleep in heavenly peace.

Silent night! Holy night!
Shepherds quake at the sight;
Glories stream from heaven afar,
Heavenly hosts sing Alleluya:
 Christ the Saviour is born,
  Christ the Saviour is born.

Silent night! Holy night!
 Son of God, love's pure light;
  Radiance beams from thy holy face,
   With the dawn of redeeming grace;
    Jesus, Lord, at Thy birth,
     Jesus, Lord, at Thy birth.

Joseph Mohr
(trans. Anon.)

Lullaby Carol

Mary sang to her pretty baby
Sleep, little one, sleep,
And all the bright angels
Of heaven sang with her
Sleep, little one, sleep.

Some shepherds heard them in the fields
Where they were watching their sheep,
They went to the stable
And joined in the carol
Sleep, little one, sleep.

From faraway lands came kings
Over the mountains so steep,
With gifts for the baby
They joined in the carol
Sleep, little one, sleep.

Sleep, little one, sleep,
Close your eyes and don't peep,
Your father and mother
Are watching your cradle
Sleep, little one, sleep.

Gerard Benson

Hark! The Herald Angels Sing

Hark! the herald angels sing
Glory to the newborn King,
Peace on earth and mercy mild,
God and sinners reconciled.
Joyful all ye nations rise,
Join the triumph of the skies;
With th'angelic host proclaim:
"Christ is born in Bethlehem."
Hark! the herald angels sing
Glory to the newborn King.

Christ, by highest Heav'n adored,
Christ, the Everlasting Lord,
Late in time behold Him come,
Offspring of a virgin's womb.
Veiled in flesh the Godhead see,
Hail the incarnate Deity!
Pleased as Man with man to dwell,
Jesus, our Emmanuel.
Hark! the herald angels sing
Glory to the newborn King.

Hail, the heaven-born Prince of Peace!
Hail, the Sun of Righteousness!
Light and life to all He brings,
Risen with healing in His wings.
Mild He lays His glory by,
Born that man no more may die,
Born to raise the sons of earth,
Born to give them second birth.
Hark! the herald angels sing
Glory to the newborn King.

Charles Wesley and others

Just Doing My Job

I'm one of Herod's Henchmen.
We don't have much to say,
We just charge through the audience
In a Henchman sort of way.

We all wear woolly helmets
To hide our hair and ears,
And Wellingtons sprayed silver
To match our tinfoil spears.

Our swords are made of cardboard
So blood will not be spilled
If we trip and stab a parent
When the hall's completely filled.

We don't look *very* scary,
We're mostly small and shy,
And some of us wear glasses,
But we give the thing a try.

We whisper Henchman noises
While Herod hunts for strangers,
And then we all charge out again
Like nervous Power Rangers.

Yet when the play is over
And Miss is out of breath
We'll charge like Henchmen through the hall
And scare our mums to death.

Clare Bevan

We Three Kings

We three kings of Orient are;
Bearing gifts we traverse afar;
Field and fountain, moor and mountain,
Following yonder star.

O star of wonder, star of night,
Star with royal beauty bright,
Westward leading still proceeding,
Guide us to thy perfect light.

Melchior:

Born a king on Bethlehem plain,
Gold I bring, to crown him again—
King for ever, ceasing never,
Over us all to reign.

Caspar:

Frankincense to offer have I;
Incense owns a Deity nigh:
Prayer and praising, all men raising,
Worship him, God most high.

Balthazar:

Myrrh is mine; its bitter perfume
Breathes a life of gathering gloom,
Sorrowing, sighing, bleeding, dying,
Sealed in the stone-cold tomb.

Glorious now, behold him arise;
King, and God, and sacrifice.
Heaven sings alleluya,
Alleluya the earth replies.

John Henry Hopkins

The Meeting Place

(after Rubens: The Adoration of the Magi, 1634)

It was the arrival of the kings
that caught us unawares;
we'd look in on the woman in the barn,
curiosity you could call it,
something to do on a cold winter's night;
we'd wished her well—
that was the best we could do, she was in pain,
and the next thing we knew
she was lying on the straw
—the little there was of it—
and there was a baby in her arms.

It was, as I say, the kings
that caught us unawares . . .
Women have babies every other day,
not that we are there—
let's call it a common occurrence though,
giving birth. But kings
appearing in a stable with a
"Is this the place?" and kneeling,
each with his gift held out towards the child!

They didn't even notice us.
Their robes trailed on the floor,
rich, lined robes that money couldn't buy.
What must this child be
to bring kings from distant lands
with costly incense and gold?
What could a tiny baby make of that?

And what were we to make of
was it angels falling through the air,
entwined and falling as if from the rafters
to where the gaze of the kings met the child's
—assuming the child could see?
What would the mother do with the gift?
What would become of the child?
And we'll never admit there are angels
or that somewhere between
one man's eyes and another's
is a holy place, a space where a king could be
at one with a naked child,
at one with an astonished soldier.

Christopher Pilling

I Saw Three Ships

I saw three ships come sailing in,
On Christmas Day, on Christmas Day,
I saw three ships come sailing in,
On Christmas Day in the morning.

And what was in those ships all three?
On Christmas Day . . .

Our Saviour Christ and His lady.
On Christmas Day . . .

Pray, whither sailed those ships all three?
On Christmas Day . . .

O, they sailed into Bethlehem.
On Christmas Day . . .

And all the bells on earth shall ring,
On Christmas Day . . .

And all the angels in Heaven shall sing,
On Christmas Day . . .

And all the souls on earth shall sing,
On Christmas Day . . .

Then let us all rejoice amain!
On Christmas Day . . .

Traditional

Now Bring Us Some Figgy Pudding

Christmas Celebrations

Keeping Christmas

How will you your Christmas keep?
Feasting, fasting, or asleep?
Will you laugh or will you pray,
Or will you forget the day?

Be it kept with joy or pray'r,
Keep of either some to spare;
Whatsoever brings the day,
Do not keep but give away.

Eleanor Farjeon

Paddington's Christmas

by Michael Bond

Paddington found that Christmas took a long time to come. Each morning when he hurried downstairs he crossed the date off the calendar, but the more days he crossed off the farther away it seemed.

However, there was plenty to occupy his mind. For one thing, the postman started arriving later and later in the morning, and when he did finally reach the Browns' house there were so many letters to deliver he had a job to push them all through the letterbox. Often there were mysterious-looking parcels as well, which Mrs Bird promptly hid before Paddington had time to squeeze them.

A surprising number of the envelopes were addressed to Paddington himself, and he carefully made a list of all those who had sent him Christmas cards so that he could be sure of thanking them.

"You may be only a small bear," said Mrs Bird, as she helped him arrange the cards on the mantelpiece, "but you certainly leave your mark."

Paddington wasn't sure how to take

this, especially as Mrs Bird had just polished the hall floor, but when he examined his paws they were quite clean.

Paddington had made his own Christmas cards. Some he had drawn himself, decorating the edges with holly and mistletoe; others had been made out of pictures cut from Mrs Brown's magazines. But each one had the words A MERRY CHRISTMAS AND A HAPPY NEW YEAR printed on the front, and they were signed PADINGTUN BROWN on the inside—together with his special paw mark to show that they were genuine.

Paddington wasn't sure about the spelling of A MERRY CHRISTMAS. It didn't look at all right. But Mrs Bird checked all the words in a dictionary for him to make certain.

"I don't suppose many people get Christmas cards from a bear," she explained. "They'll probably want to keep them, so you ought to make sure they are right."

One evening Mr Brown arrived home with a huge Christmas tree tied to the roof of his car. It was placed in a position of honour by the dining-room window and both Paddington and Mr Brown spent a long

time decorating it with coloured electric lights and silver tinsel.

Apart from the Christmas tree, there were paper chains and holly to be put up, and large coloured bells made of crinkly paper. Paddington enjoyed doing the paper chains. He managed to persuade Mr Brown that bears were very good at putting up decorations and together they did most of the house, with Paddington standing on Mr Brown's shoulders while Mr Brown handed up the drawing pins. It came to an unhappy end one evening when Paddington accidentally put his paw on a drawing pin which he'd left on top of Mr Brown's head. When Mrs Bird rushed into the dining-room to see what all the fuss was about, and to inquire why all the lights had suddenly gone out, she found Paddington hanging by his paws from the chandelier and Mr Brown dancing around the room rubbing his head.

But by then the decorations were almost finished and the house had taken on quite a festive air. The sideboard was groaning under the weight of nuts and oranges, dates and figs, none of which Paddington was allowed to touch, and Mr Brown had stopped smoking his pipe and was filling the air instead with the smell of cigars.

The excitement in the Browns' house mounted, until it reached fever pitch a few days before Christmas, when Jonathan and Judy arrived home for the holidays.

But if the days leading up to Christmas were busy and exciting, they were nothing compared with Christmas Day itself.

The Browns were up early on Christmas morning—much earlier than they had intended. It all started when Paddington woke to find a large pillowcase at the bottom of his bed. His eyes nearly popped out with astonishment when he switched his torch on, for it was bulging with parcels, and it certainly hadn't been there when he'd gone to bed on

Christmas Eve. Paddington's eyes grew larger and larger as he unwrapped the brightly coloured paper round each present. A few days before, on Mrs Bird's instructions, he had made a list of all the things he hoped to have given him and had hidden it up one of the chimneys. It was a strange thing, but everything on that list seemed to be in the pillowcase.

There was a large chemistry outfit from Mr Brown, full of jars and bottles and test tubes, which looked very interesting. And there was a miniature xylophone from Mrs Brown, which pleased him no end. Paddington was fond of music—especially the loud sort, which was good for conducting—and he had always wanted something he could actually play.

Mrs Bird's parcel was even more exciting, for it contained a checked cap which he'd specially asked for and had underlined on his list. Paddington stood on the end of his bed, admiring the effect in the mirror for quite a while.

Jonathan and Judy had each given him a travel book. Paddington was very interested in geography, being a much-travelled bear, and he was pleased to see there were plenty of maps and coloured pictures inside.

The noise from Paddington's room was soon sufficient to wake both Jonathan and Judy, and in no time at all the whole house was in an uproar, with wrapping paper and bits of string everywhere.

"I'm as patriotic as the next man," grumbled Mr Brown. "But I draw the line when bears start playing the National Anthem at six o'clock in the morning—especially on a xylophone."

As always, it was left to Mrs Bird to restore order. "No more presents until after lunch," she said firmly. She had just tripped over Paddington on the upstairs landing, where he was investigating his new chemical outfit, and something nasty had gone in one of her slippers.

"It's all right, Mrs Bird," said Paddington, consulting his instruction book, "it's only some iron filings. I don't think they're dangerous."

"Dangerous or not," said Mrs Bird, "I've a big dinner to cook— not to mention your birthday cake to finish decorating."

Being a bear, Paddington had two birthdays each year—one in the summer and one at Christmas—and the Browns were holding a party in his honour to which Mr Gruber had been invited.

After they'd had breakfast and been to church, the morning passed quickly and Paddington spent most of his time trying to decide what to do next. With so many things from which to choose it was most difficult. He read some chapters from his books and made several interesting smells and a small explosion with his chemical outfit.

Mr Brown was already in trouble for having given it to him, especially when Paddington found a chapter in the instruction book headed "Indoor Fireworks". He made himself a "never

ending" snake which wouldn't stop growing and frightened Mrs Bird to death when she met it coming down the stairs.

"If we don't watch out," she confided to Mrs Brown, "we shan't last over Christmas. We shall either be blown to smithereens or poisoned. He was testing my gravy with some litmus paper just now."

Mrs Brown sighed. "It's a good job Christmas only comes once a year," she said as she helped Mrs Bird with the potatoes.

"It isn't over yet," warned Mrs Bird.

Fortunately Mr Gruber arrived at that moment and some measure of order was established before they all sat down to dinner.

Paddington's eyes glistened as he surveyed the table. He didn't agree with Mr Brown when he said it all looked too good to eat. All the same, even Paddington got noticeably slower towards the end when Mrs Bird brought in the Christmas pudding.

"Well," said Mr Gruber, a few minutes later, as he sat back and

surveyed his empty plate, "I must say that's the best Christmas dinner I've had for many a day. Thank you very much indeed!"

"Hear! Hear!" agreed Mr Brown. "What do you say, Paddington?"

"It was very nice," said Paddington, licking some cream from his whiskers. "Except I had a bone in my Christmas pudding."

"You *what*?" exclaimed Mrs Brown. "Don't be silly—there are no bones in Christmas pudding."

"I had one," said Paddington, firmly. "It was all hard—and it stuck in my throat."

"Good gracious!" exclaimed Mrs Bird. "The five pence! I always put a piece of silver in the Christmas pudding."

"What!" said Paddington, nearly falling off his chair. "A five pence? I've never heard of a five pence pudding before."

"Quick," shouted Mr Brown, rising to the emergency. "Turn him upside down."

Before Paddington could reply, he found himself hanging head downwards while Mr Brown and Mr Gruber took it in turns to shake him. The rest of the family stood round watching the floor.

"It's no good," said Mr Brown, after a while. "It must have gone too far." He helped Mr Gruber lift Paddington into an armchair, where he lay gasping for breath.

"I've got a magnet upstairs," said Jonathan. "We could try lowering it down his throat on a piece of string."

"I don't think so, dear," said Mrs Brown, in a worried tone of voice. "He might swallow that and then we should be even worse off." She bent over the chair. "How do you feel, Paddington?"

"Sick," said Paddington, in an aggrieved tone of voice.

"Of course you do, dear," said Mrs Brown. "It's only to be expected. There's only one thing to do—we shall have to send for the doctor."

"Thank goodness I scrubbed it first," said Mrs Bird. "It might have been covered with germs."

"But I *didn't* swallow it," gasped Paddington. "I only nearly did. Then I put it on the side of my plate. I didn't know it was five pence because it was all covered with Christmas pudding."

Paddington felt very fed up. He'd just eaten one of the best dinners he could ever remember and now he'd been turned upside down and shaken without even being given time to explain.

Everyone exchanged glances and then crept quietly away, leaving Paddington to recover by himself. There didn't seem to be much they *could* say.

But after the dinner things had been cleared away, and by the time Mrs Bird had made some strong coffee, Paddington was almost himself again. He was sitting up in the chair helping himself to some dates when they trooped back into the room. It took a lot to make Paddington ill for very long.

Here We Come A-Wassailing

Here we come a-wassailing
    Among the leaves so green,
Here we come a-wandering,
    So fair to be seen:

    Love and joy come to you,
        And to you your wassail too,
    And God bless you, and send you
    A happy new year.

We have got a little purse
    Of stretching leather skin;
We want a little of your money
    To line it well within.

Bring us out a table,
    And spread it with a cloth;
Bring us out a mouldy cheese,
    And some of your Christmas loaf.

God bless the master of this house,
    Likewise the mistress too;
And all the little children
    That round the table go.

Good Master and good Mistress,
    While you're sitting by the fire,
Pray think of us poor children
    Who are wandering in the mire.

Traditional

Christmas To Me Was Snow

Christmas to me
was snow
but it never snowed
it always rained
or was sunny.
Once it snowed
and that was Christmas.
But the turkey got burnt
and when you chewed it
Mum said "Do you like it?"
and you said "Yes"
and that was her Christmas.
Dad's was a cigar
or an ounce of St Bruno or new slippers.

Thomas Boyle (aged 14)

The Christmas Pudding

Into the basin
put the plums,
Stir-about, stir-about,
    stir-about!

Next the good
white flour comes,
Stir about, stir-about,
    stir-about!

Sugar and peel
and eggs and spice,
Stir-about, stir-about,
    stir-about!

Mix them and fix them
and cook them twice,
Stir-about, stir-about,
    stir-about!

Anon.

Good Will to Men—
Christmas Greetings in Six Languages

At Christmas, when old friends are meeting,
We give that long-loved joyous greeting—
   "Merry Christmas!"

While hanging sheaves for winter birds
Friends in Norway call the words,
   "God Jul!"

With wooden shoes ranged on the hearth,
Dutch celebrators cry their mirth,
   "Vrolyk Kerstfeest!"

In France, that land of courtesy,
Our welcome to our guests would be,
   "Joyeux Noël!"

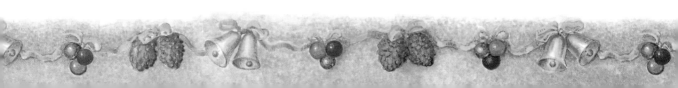

Enshrining Christmas in her art,
Italy cries from a full heart,
    "Buon Natale!"

When in the land of Christmas trees,
Old Germany, use words like these—
    "Fröhliche Weihnachten!"

Though each land names a different name,
Good will rings through each wish the same—
    "Merry Christmas!"

Dorothy Brown Thompson

Pippi Longstocking's Christmas

by Astrid Lindgren

Pippi Longstocking is an amazing little girl. Although she's only nine years old, she lives by herself in Villekulla Cottage. Her many friends include Mr Nilsson (her pet monkey) and Tommy and Annika who live next door. The most amazing thing about Pippi is her strength. She is so strong she can even lift up her horse! In this story, Pippi, Tommy and Annika have returned from a trip to the South Sea Island where Pippi's father is king. It's the beginning of January, but not too late for Christmas celebrations!

When they reached the garden gate of Villekulla Cottage they stopped short and could hardly believe their eyes. The picture they saw was just like a Christmas card. The whole house was covered in soft snow and there were cheerful lights shining from every window. The flame of a burning torch outside the front door threw flickering beams across the gleaming snow. The path had been cleared, so

Tommy and Annika could now walk up to the porch without sinking into drifts of snow.

They were just stamping the snow off their boots in the porch when the door opened, and there stood Pippi.

"A happy Christmas to you in this cottage," she said. Then she pushed them into the kitchen. Heavens! If there wasn't a Christmas tree! The candles were lit, and seventeen sparklers, hooked onto the Christmas tree, were burning and spluttering and giving out a lovely smell. The table was laden with every kind of Christmas food: a large ham, coated in breadcrumbs, and decorated with fringes of tissue-paper, home-made sausages, and Christmas pudding. Pippi had even made ginger biscuits, in the shapes of boys and girls, and saffron bread. A roaring fire burned in the kitchen range, and close to the wood box stood the horse, pawing the floor delicately with his foot. Mr Nilsson was jumping about in the tree in between the sparklers.

"He's supposed to be the Christmas angel," said Pippi, severely, "but do you think I can get him to sit still at the top?"

Tommy and Annika were speechless.

"Oh, Pippi," said Annika at last, "how beautiful! But how did you manage to do it all in the time?"

"I have an industrious disposition," said Pippi.

Tommy and Annika were filled with sudden joy and happiness.

"I *am* glad we're home at Villekulla Cottage again," said Tommy.

They sat down at the table and ate their fill of ham, sausages, pudding, ginger biscuits, and saffron bread, and they thought the feast tasted even better than bananas and breadfruit.

"But Pippi! It isn't Christmas time," said Tommy.

"Yes, it is," said Pippi. "Villekulla Cottage's calendar has lost a lot of time. I shall have to take it to a calendar repairer and have it seen to, so that it catches up again."

"*What* a good thing!" said Annika. "So we didn't miss our Christmas, after all—though, of course, we didn't get any presents."

"Ah, I was thinking the very same thing," said Pippi. "I've hidden your presents. You'll have to look for them."

Tommy and Annika went red in the face with excitement. Before you could wink twice they got up from the table and started hunting. In the wood box Tommy found a large parcel; on it was written TOMMY. It contained a splendid paint-box. Underneath the table Annika found a parcel with her name on it, and inside the parcel was a pretty red sun-shade.

"I shall take it with me next time we go to Canny Canny Island," said Annika.

Inside the chimney corner hung two parcels. One contained a toy jeep for Tommy, and the other, a doll's tea-service for Annika. A little parcel was hanging from the horse's tail and in it was a clock for the mantelpiece of Tommy and Annika's nursery.

When they had found all their presents they both gave Pippi a big hug. She was standing by the kitchen window, looking at the quantities of snow in the garden.

"Tomorrow, we're going to build a big igloo," she said, "And we'll have a candle burning in it in the evenings."

"Oh yes, let's," said Annika, feeling more and more pleased to be home again.

"And let's make a ski-slope running down from the roof and into the snow below," said Pippi. "I want to teach the horse to ski, but I'm blowed if I know whether he will need four skis, or only two."

"Hurray! We're going to have a lovely time tomorrow," said Tommy. "Wasn't it lucky we came in the middle of the Christmas hols?"

"We shall always have a lovely time here at Villekulla Cottage and on Canny Canny Island and everywhere," said Annika.

Pippi nodded in agreement. All three were now sitting on the kitchen table. A shadow suddenly passed across Tommy's face.

"I never want to grow up," he said firmly.

"Nor me," said Annika.

"No, that's nothing to pine for," said Pippi. "Grown-ups never have any fun. All they have is a lot of dull work and stupid clothes and corns and nincum tax."

"It's called income tax," said Annika.

"It's all the same rubbish," said Pippi. "And they're full of superstition and silly ideas. They think it's bad luck to put a knife in your mouth when you eat, and things like that."

"And they don't know how to play," said Annika. "Ugh! Fancy having to grow up!"

"And who said we have to?" asked Pippi. "If I remember rightly, I've got some pills somewhere."

"What kind of pills?" said Tommy.

"Awfully good pills for those who don't want to grow up," said Pippi, jumping down from the table. She searched in all the cupboards and drawers, and after a short time she brought out what looked exactly like three yellow dried peas.

"Peas!" said Tommy in surprise.

"That's what *you* think," said Pippi. "It isn't peas. It's squigglypills. An old Red Indian Chief gave them to me a long time ago in Rio when I happened to mention that I didn't care very much for growing up."

"Is that all you have to do—just take those little pills?" asked Annika doubtfully.

"Yes," Pippi assured her. "But you must eat them in the dark and say: 'Little squiggle, you are clever, I do not want to *grew* up ever.'"

"You mean 'grow', don't you?" said Tommy.

"I said 'grew', and I mean 'grew'," said Pippi. "That's the whole secret, you see. Most people say 'grow' and that's the worst thing you can do, because it makes you grow more than ever. Once there was a boy who ate pills like these. He said 'grow' instead of 'grew' and he began to grow so much it was frightening. Lots and lots of yards every day. It was tragic. Mind you, it was all very well so long as he could walk about and graze straight out of big apple trees, rather like a giraffe. But it wasn't long before he got too tall for that. When his aunts came on a visit and they wanted to say: 'What a fine big fellow you've grown into', they had to shout to him through a megaphone. All you could see of him was his long thin legs, like two flagpoles, which disappeared in the clouds. We never heard a sound from him again except once, when he took it into his head to lick the sun and got a blister on his tongue. Then he yelled so loudly that the flowers down on Earth all wilted. That was the very last sign of life we ever had from him. But I suppose his legs are still walking about in Rio and causing a lot of disturbance in the traffic, if I'm not much mistaken."

"I daren't take a pill," said Annika, frightened, "in case I say the wrong thing."

"You won't," said Pippi, consolingly. "If I thought you'd do that, I wouldn't let you have one, because it would be so dull to have only your legs to play with. Tommy and me and your legs—that would be a queer sight!"

"Don't be silly, Annika," said Tommy. "Of course you won't say it wrong."

They blew out all the candles on the Christmas tree. The kitchen was quite dark except near the stove, where you could see the fire glowing behind the bars. The children sat down silently in a circle in the middle of the floor. They held hands. Pippi gave Tommy and Annika a squigglypill each. They could feel the excitement creeping up and down their spines. Imagine it—in a moment or two they would have swallowed the strange pills and then they would never, never have to grow up. Wasn't it wonderful?

"Now!" whispered Pippi.

They swallowed their pills, saying, all three together:

"Little squiggle, you are clever,
I do not want to grew up ever."

It was all over. Pippi lit the lamp.

"Good!" she said. "Now we shan't have to grow up and have corns and other miseries. Of course, the pills have been in my cupboard for so long that I can't be *quite* sure they haven't lost their goodness. But we must hope for the best."

Something had just occurred to Annika.

"But Pippi!" she cried in dismay, "you were going to be a pirate when you grew up!"

"Oh, I can be a pirate anyway," said Pippi. "I can be a teeny-weeny ferocious pirate, spreading death and destruction, all the same."

She looked thoughtful.

"Supposing," she said, "supposing that after many, many years have gone by, a lady comes walking past here one day and sees us running in the garden and playing. Perhaps she will ask you, Tommy, 'And how old are you, my little friend?' And you say: 'Fifty-three, if I'm not mistaken.'"

Tommy laughed heartily.

"I shall be rather small for my age, I think," he said.

"Yes," admitted Pippi, "but you can always say that you were bigger when you were smaller."

Tommy and Annika now remembered that their mother had told them not to stay long.

"I'm afraid we've got to go home," said Tommy.

"But we'll be back tomorrow," said Annika.

"Good," said Pippi. "We're starting on the igloo at eight o'clock."

She saw them off at the gate and her red plaits bobbed round her head as she ran back to Villekulla Cottage.

"Well!" said Tommy a little later when he was brushing his teeth. "If I hadn't known they were squigglypills I could have sworn they were just ordinary peas."

Annika was standing by the nursery window in her pink pyjamas, looking towards Villekulla Cottage.

"Look! I can see Pippi!" she shouted in delight.

Tommy rushed to the window. Yes! So could he! Now that the trees were bare you could see right into Pippi's kitchen.

Pippi was sitting by the table, leaning her head on her arms. She was gazing dreamily at the flickering light of a small candle in front of her.

"She's . . . she's looking so lonely, somehow," said Annika; and her voice trembled a little. "Oh, Tommy, I wish it was morning and we could go to her straight away."

They stood there, silently looking out into the winter night. The stars were shining above the roof of Villekulla Cottage and Pippi was inside. She would always be there. It was wonderful to remember that. The years would pass, but Pippi and Tommy and Annika would never grow up. That is, if the squigglypills were still good!

We Wish You A Merry Christmas

We wish you a merry Christmas,
We wish you a merry Christmas,
We wish you a merry Christmas,
And a happy New Year.

Good tidings we bring
To you and your kin,
We wish you a merry Christmas,
And a happy New Year.

Now bring us some figgy pudding,
Now bring us some figgy pudding,
Now bring us some figgy pudding,
And bring some out here.

For we all like figgy pudding,
For we all like figgy pudding,
For we all like figgy pudding,
So bring some out here.

And we won't go until we've had some,
And we won't go until we've had some,
And we won't go until we've had some,
So bring some out here.

Traditional

Little Donkey

Christmas Animals

What the Donkey Saw

No room in the inn, of course,
And not that much in the stable,
What with the shepherds, Magi, Mary,
Joseph, the heavenly host—
Not to mention the baby
Using our manger as a cot.
You couldn't have squeezed another cherub in
For love or money.

Still, in spite of the overcrowding,
I did my best to make them feel wanted.
I could see the baby and I
Would be going places together.

U. A. Fanthorpe

Christmas Morn

Shall I tell you what will come
to Bethlehem on Christmas morn,
who will kneel them gently down
before the Lord new-born?

One small fish from the river,
with scales of red, red gold,
one wild bee from the heather,
one grey lamb from the fold,
one ox from the high pasture,
one black bull from the herd,
one goatling from the far hills,
one white, white bird.

And many children—God give them grace,
bringing tall candles to light Mary's face.

Ruth Sawyer

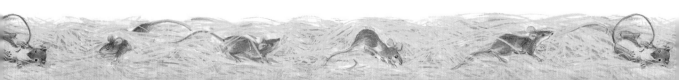

The Friendly Beasts

Jesus, our brother, kind and good,
Was humbly born in a stable rude,
And the friendly beasts around Him stood;
Jesus, our brother, kind and good.

"I," said the donkey, shaggy and brown,
"I carried His mother up hill and down;
I carried her safely to Bethlehem town;
I," said the donkey, shaggy and brown.

"I," said the cow, all white and red,
"I gave Him my manger for His bed;
I gave Him my hay to pillow His head;
I," said the cow, all white and red.

"I," said the sheep with curly horn,

"I gave Him my wool for His blanket warm.

He wore my coat on Christmas morn.

I," said the sheep with curly horn.

"I," said the dove from the rafters high,

"Cooed Him to sleep, that He should not cry,

We cooed Him to sleep, my mate and I.

I," said the dove from the rafters high.

Thus every beast by some good spell,

In the stable dark was glad to tell

Of the gift he gave Emmanuel,

The gift he gave Emmanuel.

Traditional

Mrs Christmas

She was about as small as a cup
But big as your hand when she grew up
And she came to stay on Christmas Day
So we called her Mrs Christmas.

She liked to swoop around the hall
With a silver paper soccer ball
And I think I was four but maybe some more
When I named her Mrs Christmas.

She had some kittens with bright white socks
And she kept them out in a brown cardboard box
And she'd nudge them out and march them about
Saying: "I am Mrs Christmas."

Adrian Mitchell

Small, Smaller

I thought that I knew all there was to know
Of being small, until I saw once, black against the snow,
A shrew, trapped in my footprint, jump and fall
And jump again and fall, the hole too deep, the walls too tall.

Russell Hoban

The Christmas Day Kitten

by James Herriot

Christmas can never go by without my remembering a certain little cat. I first saw her when I called to see one of Mrs Pickering's much-loved Basset hounds.

I looked in some surprise at the furry creature moving quietly down the hall.

"I didn't know you had a cat," I said to Mrs Pickering, who was a plumpish, pleasant-faced woman.

Mrs Pickering smiled. "We haven't really. Debbie is a stray. She comes here two or three times a week and we give her some food. I don't know where she lives."

"Do you ever get the feeling that she wants to stay with you?" I asked.

"No." Mrs Pickering shook her head. "She's a timid little thing. Just creeps in, has some food, then slips away. She doesn't seem to want to let me help her in any way."

I looked at the little tabby cat again. "But she isn't just having food today."

"It's a funny thing, but every now and

again she pops through into the sitting-room and sits by the fire for a few minutes. It's as though she was giving herself a treat."

The little cat was sitting very upright on the thick rug which lay in front of the fireplace in which the coals glowed and flamed. The three Bassets were already lying there but they seemed used to Debbie because two of them sniffed her in a bored manner and the third merely cocked a sleepy eye at her before flopping back to sleep.

Debbie made no effort to curl up or wash herself or do anything other than gaze quietly ahead. This was obviously a special event in her life, a treat.

Then suddenly she turned and crept from the room without a sound, and was gone.

"That's just the way it is with Debbie," said Mrs Pickering, laughing. "She never stays more than ten minutes or so, then she's off."

I often visited the Pickering home and I always looked out for the little cat. On one occasion I spotted her nibbling daintily from a saucer at the kitchen door. As I watched, she turned and almost floated on light footsteps into the hall, then through into the sitting-room.

Debbie settled herself in the middle of the pile of Basset hounds in her usual way: upright, still, and gazing into the glowing fire.

This time, I tried to make friends with her but she leaned away as I stretched out my hand. However, I talked to her softly and I managed to stroke her cheek with one finger.

Then it was time for her to go and, once outside the house, she jumped up onto the stone wall and down the other side. The last I saw was the little tabby figure flitting away across the grassy field.

"I wonder where she goes?" I murmured.

"That's something we've never been able to find out," said Mrs Pickering.

It was three months later that I next heard from Mrs Pickering—and it happened to be Christmas morning.

"I'm so sorry to bother you today of all days," said Mrs Pickering apologetically.

"Don't worry at all," I said. "Which of the dogs needs attention?"

"It's not the dogs. It's ... Debbie. She's come to the house and there's something very wrong. Please come quickly."

I drove through the empty market square. The snow was thick on the road and on the roofs of the surrounding houses. The shops were closed but the pretty coloured lights of the Christmas trees winked in the windows.

Mrs Pickering's house was beautifully decorated with tinsel and holly, and the rich smell of turkey and sage and onion stuffing wafted from the

kitchen. But she had a very worried look on her face as she led me through to the sitting-room.

Debbie was there, but she wasn't sitting upright in her usual position. She was lying quite still—and huddled close to her lay a tiny kitten.

I looked down in amazement. "What have we got here?"

"It's the strangest thing," Mrs Pickering replied. "I haven't seen her for several weeks and then she came in about two hours ago, staggered into the kitchen, and she was carrying the kitten in her mouth. She brought it in here and laid it on the rug. Almost immediately I could see that she wasn't well. Then she lay down like this and she hasn't moved since."

I knelt on the rug and passed my hand over Debbie's body which Mrs Pickering had placed on a piece of sheet. She was very, very thin and her coat was dirty. I knew that she didn't have long to live.

"Is she ill, Mr Herriot?" asked Mrs Pickering in a trembling voice.

"Yes . . . yes, I'm afraid so. But I don't think she is in any pain."

Mrs Pickering looked at me and I saw there were tears in her eyes. Then she knelt beside Debbie and stroked the cat's head while the tears fell on the dirty fur.

"Oh, the poor little thing! I should have done more for her."

I spoke gently. "Nobody could have done more than you. Nobody could have been kinder. And see, she has brought her kitten to you, hasn't she?"

"Yes, you are right, she has." Mrs Pickering reached out and lifted up the tiny, bedraggled kitten. "Isn't it strange—Debbie knew she was dying so she brought her kitten here. And on Christmas Day."

I bent down and put my hand on Debbie's heart. There was no beat. "I'm afraid she has died." I lifted the feather-light body, wrapped it in the piece of sheet and took it out to the car.

When I came back, Mrs Pickering was still stroking the kitten. The tears had dried, and she was bright-eyed as she looked at me.

"I've never had a cat before," she said.

I smiled. "Well, it looks as though you've got one now."

And she certainly had. The kitten grew rapidly into a sleek, handsome and bouncy tabby cat and Mrs Pickering called him Buster. He wasn't timid like his little mother and he lived like a king—and with the ornate collar he always wore, looked like one too.

I watched him grow up with delight, but the occasion that always stays in my mind was the following Christmas Day, a year after his arrival.

I was on my way home after visiting a farmer with a sick cow, and I was looking forward to my Christmas dinner. Mrs Pickering was at her front door when I passed her house and I heard her call out, "Merry Christmas, Mr Herriot! Come in and have a drink to warm you up."

I had a little time to spare, so I stopped the car and went in. In the house there was all the festive cheer of last year and the same glorious whiff of sage and onion stuffing. But this year, there was no sorrow—there was Buster!

He was darting up to each of the Basset hounds in turn, ears pricked, eyes twinkling, dabbing a paw at them, and then streaking away.

Mrs Pickering laughed. "Buster does tease them so. He gives them no peace."

She was right. For a long time, the dogs had led a rather sedate life: gentle walks with their mistress, plenty of good food, and long snoring sessions on the rugs and armchairs. Then Buster arrived.

He was now dancing up to the youngest dog again, head on one side, asking him to play. When he started boxing with both paws, it was too much for the Basset who rolled over with the cat in a wrestling game.

"Come into the garden," said Mrs Pickering. "I want to show you something."

She lifted a hard rubber ball from the sideboard and we went outside.

She threw the ball across the lawn and Buster bounded after it over the frosty grass, his tabby coat gleaming in the sun. He seized the ball in his mouth, brought it back to his mistress, dropped it at her feet, and waited. Mrs Pickering threw it and again Buster brought it back.

I gasped. A retriever-cat!

The Bassets looked on unimpressed. Nothing would ever make *them* chase a ball, but Buster did it again and again as though he would never tire of it.

Mrs Pickering turned to me. "Have you ever seen anything like that?"

"No," I replied. "He is a most remarkable cat."

We went back into the house where she held Buster close to her, laughing as the big cat purred loudly.

Looking at him, so healthy and contented, I remembered his

mother who had carried her tiny kitten to the only place of comfort and warmth that she had ever known.

Mrs Pickering was thinking the same thing because she turned to me and, although she was smiling, her eyes were thoughtful. "Debbie would be pleased," she said.

I nodded. "Yes, she would. It was just a year ago today she brought him in, wasn't it?"

"That's right." She hugged Buster again. "The best Christmas present I've ever had."

The Lamb's Story

I was the weak
Rejected one,
Left for the crows
To have their fun.

The shepherd's wife
She took me in,
Kept me warm
With her own soft skin.

Now I am tame
As a little child
Bleating at boys
On the hilltop wild.

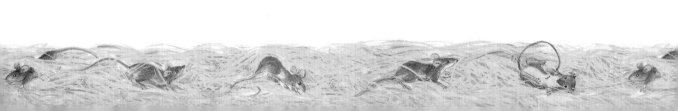

Taking my food
From anyone's hand
Free as a dog
In the midnight land.

But men with wings
Are a mystery
Their song so strange
It startles me.

I follow the crowd
To a secret place,
I watch the mother's
Weary face.

Around her feet
I softly twine,
To share my warmth
Where cold stars shine.

Her baby's cry
Is weak and thin—
May gentle strangers
Take Him in.

And when the human
Crows arrive
May kindness keep
Her lamb alive.

Clare Bevan

Little Robin Redbreast

Little Robin Redbreast
Sat upon a tree,
He sang merrily,
As merrily as could be.
He nodded with his head,
And his tail waggled he,
As little Robin Redbreast
Sat upon a tree.

Anon.

Little Donkey

Little donkey, little donkey,
On the dusty road.
Got to keep on plodding onwards,
With your precious load.
Been a long time, little donkey,
Through the winter's night.
Don't give up now, little donkey,
Bethlehem's in sight.

Ring out those bells tonight,
Bethlehem, Bethlehem.
Follow that star tonight,
Bethlehem, Bethlehem.
Little donkey, little donkey,
Had a heavy day.
Little donkey, carry Mary safely on her way.

Little donkey, little donkey,
On the dusty road.
There are wise men waiting for a
Sign to bring them here.
Do not falter, little donkey,
There's a star ahead.
It will guide you, little donkey,
To a cattle shed.

Traditional

The Shepherd's Dog

Out on the windy hill
Under that sudden star
A blaze of radiant light
Frightened my master.

He got up, left our sheep,
Tramped over the moor.
And I, following,
Came to this open door,

Sidled in, settled down,
Head on my paws,
Glad to be here, away
From the wind's sharpness.

Such warmth is in this shed,
Such comfort from this Child,
That I forget my hard life,
Ignore the harsh world,

And see on my master's face
The same joy I possess,
The knowledge of peace,
True happiness.

Leslie Norris

The Birds' Carol

From out of a wood did a cuckoo fly,
    Cuckoo.
He came to a manger with joyful cry,
    Cuckoo;
He hopped, he curtsied, round he flew,
And loud his jubilation grew,
    Cuckoo, cuckoo, cuckoo.

A pigeon flew over to Galilee,
    Vrercroo.
He strutted, and cooed, and was full of glee,
    Vrercroo.
And showed with jewelled wings unfurled,
His joy that Christ was in the world,
    Vrercroo, vrercroo, vrercroo.

A dove settled down upon Nazareth,
    Tsucroo.
And tenderly chanted with all his breath,
    Tsucroo.
"O you," he cooed, "so good and true,
My beauty do I give to you—
    Tsucroo, tsucroo, tsucroo."

Traditional Czech Carol
translation by Percy Dearmer

A Partridge in a Pear Tree

Christmas Presents

Reindeer Report

Chimneys: colder.
Flightpaths: busier.
Driver: Christmas (F)
Still baffled by postcodes.

Children: more
And stay up later.
Presents: heavier.
Pay: frozen.

Mission in spite
Of all this
Accomplished.

U. A. Fanthorpe

Santa's Sad Sack

When Santa reached
inside his sack,
he pulled out a grubby
anorak,

a smelly welly,
some dirty socks
and a mangled plastic
sandwich box.

"Oh, no . . ." said Santa,
beginning to sag.
"I've brought the Gnomes'
Lost Property Bag!"

Tony Mitton

The Naughtiest Story of All

by Dorothy Edwards

This is such a very terrible story about my naughty little sister that I hardly know how to tell it to you. It is all about one Christmas-time.

Now, my naughty little sister was very pleased when Christmas began to draw near, because she liked all the excitement of the plum-puddings and the turkeys, and the crackers and the holly, and all the Christmassy-looking shops, but there was one very awful thing about her—she didn't like to think about Father Christmas at all—she said he was a horrid old man!

There—I knew you would be shocked at that. But she did. And she said she wouldn't put up her stocking for him.

My mother told my naughty little sister what a good old man Father Christmas was, and how he brought the toys along on Christmas Eve, but my naughty little sister said, "I don't care. And I don't want that nasty old man coming to our house."

Well now, that was bad enough, wasn't it? But the really dreadful thing happened later on.

This is the dreadful thing: one day, my school-teacher said that a Father Christmas Man would be coming to the school to bring presents

for all the children, and my teacher said that the Father Christmas Man would have toys for all our little brothers and sisters as well, if they cared to come along for them. She said there would be a real Christmas-tree with candles on it, and sweeties and cups of tea and biscuits for our mothers.

Wasn't that a nice thought? Well now, when I told my little sister about the Christmas-tree, she said, "Oh, nice!"

And when I told her about the sweeties she said, "Very, very nice!" But when I told her about the Father Christmas Man, she said, "Don't want him, nasty old man."

Still, my mother said, "You can't go to the Christmas-tree without seeing him, so if you don't want to see him all that much, you will have to stay at home."

But my naughty little sister did want to go, very much, so she said, "I will go, and when the horrid Father Christmas Man comes in, I will close my eyes."

So, we all went to the Christmas-tree together, my mother, and I, and my naughty little sister.

When we got to the school, my naughty little sister was very pleased to see all the pretty paperchains that we had made in school hanging all around the classrooms, and when she saw all the little lanterns, and the holly, and all the robin-redbreast drawings pinned on the blackboards she smiled and smiled. She was very smiley at first.

All the mothers, and the little brothers and sisters who were too young for school, sat down in chairs and desks, and all the big schoolchildren acted a play for them.

My little sister was very excited to see all the children dressed up as fairies and robins and elves and Bo-peeps and things, and she clapped her hands very hard, like all the grown-ups did, to show that she was enjoying herself. And she still smiled.

Then, when some of the teachers came round with bags of sweets, tied up in pretty coloured paper, my little sister smiled even more, and she sang too when all the children sang. She sang, "Away in a manger", because she knew the words very well. When she didn't know the words of some of the singing, she "la-la'd".

After all the singing, the teachers put out the lights, and took away a big screen from a corner of the room, and there was the Christmas-tree, all lit up with candles and shining with silvery stuff, and little shiny coloured balls. There were lots of toys on the tree, and all the children cheered and clapped.

Then the teachers put the lights on again, and blew out the candles, so that we could all go and look at the tree. My little sister went too. She looked at the tree, and she looked at the toys, and she saw a specially nice doll with a blue dress on, and she said, "For me."

My mother said, "You must wait and see what you are given."

Then the teachers called out, "Back to your seats, everyone, we have a visitor coming." So all the children went back to their seats, and sat still and waited and listened.

And, as we waited and listened, we heard a tinkle-tinkle bell noise, and then the schoolroom door opened, and in walked the Father Christmas Man. My naughty little sister had forgotten all

about him, so she hadn't time to close her eyes before he walked in. However, when she saw him, my little sister stopped smiling and began to be stubborn.

The Father Christmas Man was very nice. He said he hoped we were having a good time, and we all said, "Yes," except my naughty little sister—she didn't say a thing.

Then he said, "Now, one at a time, children; and I will give each one of you a toy."

So, first of all each schoolchild went up for a toy, and my naughty little sister still didn't shut her eyes because she wanted to see who was going to have the specially nice doll in the blue dress. But none of the schoolchildren had it.

Then Father Christmas began to call the little brothers and sisters up

for presents, and, as he didn't know their names, he just said, "Come along, sonny," if it were a boy, and, "Come along, girlie," if it were a girl. The Father Christmas Man let the little brothers and sisters choose their own toys off the tree.

When my naughty little sister saw this, she was so worried about the specially nice doll that she thought that she would just go up and get it.

She said, "I don't like that horrid old beardy man, but I do like that nice doll."

So, my naughty little sister got up without being asked to, and she went right out to the front where the Father Christmas Man was standing, and she said, "That doll, please," and pointed to the doll she wanted.

The Father Christmas Man laughed and all the teachers laughed, and the other mothers and the schoolchildren, and all the little brothers and sisters. My mother did not laugh because she was so shocked to see my naughty little sister going out without being asked to.

The Father Christmas Man took the specially nice doll off the tree, and he handed it to my naughty little sister and he said, "Well now, I hear you don't like me very much, but won't you shake hands?" and my naughty little sister said, "No." But she took the doll all the same.

The Father Christmas Man put out his nice old hand for her to shake and be friends, and do you know what that naughty bad girl did? She bit his hand. She really and truly did. Can you think of anything more dreadful and terrible? She bit Father Christmas's good old hand, and

then she turned and ran and ran out of the school with all the children staring after her, and her doll held very tight in her arms.

The Father Christmas Man was very nice. He said it wasn't a hard bite, only a frightened one, and he made all the children sing songs together.

When my naughty little sister was brought back by my mother, she said she was very sorry, and the Father Christmas Man said, "That's all right, old lady," and because he was so smiley and nice to her, my funny little sister went right up to him, and gave him a big "sorry" kiss, which pleased him very much.

And she hung her stocking up after all, and that kind man remembered to fill it up for her.

My little sister kept the specially nice doll until she was quite grown-up. She called it Rosy-Primrose, and although she was sometimes bad-tempered with it, she really loved it very much indeed.

Santa Claus

I won't go to sleep

Fur coat, fur hat, and fur-lined gloves,
And now he pulls his snowboots on.
His sledge is piled with sacks and sacks:
I'll wish again before it's gone.

I won't go to sleep

He walks the paddock deep in snow,
He harnesses his reindeer team.
The reindeer snort and shake their heads;
Their bells and harness-buckles gleam.

I WON'T go to sleep

Their comet rises through the air;
Fast-falling snowflakes pass them by.
With silent hooves and shaken bells
They stream across the starlit sky.

I . . . won't . . . go . . . to . . .

Clive Sansom

A Visit from St Nicholas

'Twas the night before Christmas, when all through the house
Not a creature was stirring, not even a mouse;
The stockings were hung by the chimney with care,
In hopes that St Nicholas soon would be there;
The children were nestled all snug in their beds,
While visions of sugar-plums danced in their heads;
And mamma in her 'kerchief, and I in my cap,
Had just settled our brains for a long winter's nap—
When out on the lawn there arose such a clatter,
I sprang from my bed to see what was the matter.
Away to the window I flew like a flash,
Tore open the shutters, and threw up the sash.
The moon, on the breast of the new-fallen snow,
Gave the lustre of midday to objects below;
When, what to my wondering eyes should appear,
But a miniature sleigh and eight tiny reindeer,
With a little old driver, so lively and quick,
I knew in a moment it must be St Nick.

More rapid than eagles his coursers they came,
And he whistled, and shouted, and called them by name:
"Now, *Dasher*! now, *Dancer*! now, *Prancer* and *Vixen*!
On, *Comet*! on, *Cupid*! on, *Donner* and *Blitzen*!
To the top of the porch! to the top of the wall!
Now dash away! dash away! dash away all!"
As dry leaves that before the wild hurricane fly,
When they meet with an obstacle, mount to the sky;
So up to the house-top the coursers they flew
With the sleigh full of toys, and St Nicholas too.
And then, in a twinkling, I heard on the roof
The prancing and pawing of each little hoof—
As I drew in my head, and was turning around,
Down the chimney St Nicholas came with a bound.
He was dressed all in fur, from his head to his foot,
And his clothes were all tarnished with ashes and soot;
A bundle of toys he had flung on his back,
And he looked like a pedlar just opening his pack.
His eyes—how they twinkled; his dimples, how merry!
His cheeks were like roses, his nose like a cherry!

His droll little mouth was drawn up like a bow,
And the beard of his chin was as white as the snow;
The stump of a pipe he held tight in his teeth.
And the smoke it encircled his head like a wreath;
He had a broad face and a little round belly
That shook, when he laughed, like a bowl full of jelly.
He was chubby and plump, a right jolly old elf,
And I laughed when I saw him, in spite of myself,
A wink of his eye and a twist of his head
Soon gave me to know I had nothing to dread;
He spoke not a word, but went straight to his work,
And filled all the stockings; then turned with a jerk,
And laying his finger aside of his nose,
And giving a nod, up the chimney he rose;
He sprang to his sleigh, to his team gave a whistle,
And away they all flew like the down of a thistle.
But I heard him exclaim, ere he drove out of sight,
"Happy Christmas to all, and to all a good night!"

Clement Clarke Moore

Christmas Secrets

Secrets long and secrets wide,
brightly wrapped and tightly tied,

Secrets fat and secrets thin,
boxed and sealed and hidden in,

Some that rattle, some that squeak,
some that caution "Do Not Peek" . . .

Hurry, Christmas, get here first,
get here fast . . . before we *burst*.

Aileen Fisher

The Twelve Days of Christmas

The first day of Christmas
My true love sent to me
A partridge in a pear tree.

The second day of Christmas
My true love sent to me
Two turtle doves, and
A partridge in a pear tree.

The third day of Christmas
My true love sent to me
Three French hens,
Two turtle doves, and
A partridge in a pear tree.

The fourth day of Christmas
My true love sent to me
Four colly birds,
Three French hens,
Two turtle doves, and
A partridge in a pear tree.

The fifth day of Christmas
My true love sent to me
Five gold rings,
Four colly birds,
Three French hens,
Two turtle doves, and
A partridge in a pear tree.

The sixth day of Christmas
My true love sent to me
Six geese a-laying,
Five gold rings,
Four colly birds,
Three French hens,
Two turtle doves, and
A partridge in a pear tree.

The seventh day of Christmas
My true love sent to me
Seven swans a-swimming,
Six geese a-laying,
Five gold rings,
Four colly birds,
Three French hens,
Two turtle doves, and
A partridge in a pear tree.

The eighth day of Christmas
My true love sent to me
Eight maids a-milking,
Seven swans a-swimming,
Six geese a-laying,
Five gold rings,
Four colly birds,
Three French hens,
Two turtle doves, and
A partridge in a pear tree.

The ninth day of Christmas
My true love sent to me
Nine drummers drumming,
Eight maids a-milking,
Seven swans a-swimming,
Six geese a-laying,
Five gold rings,
Four colly birds,
Three French hens,
Two turtle doves, and
A partridge in a pear tree.

The tenth day of Christmas
My true love sent to me
Ten pipers piping,
Nine drummers drumming,
Eight maids a-milking,
Seven swans a-swimming,
Six geese a-laying,
Five gold rings,
Four colly birds,
Three French hens,
Two turtle doves, and
A partridge in a pear tree.

The eleventh day of Christmas
My true love sent to me
Eleven ladies dancing,
Ten pipers piping,
Nine drummers drumming,
Eight maids a-milking,
Seven swans a-swimming,
Six geese a-laying,
Five gold rings,
Four colly birds,
Three French hens,
Two turtle doves, and
A partridge in a pear tree.

The twelfth day of Christmas
My true love sent to me
Twelve lords a-leaping,
Eleven ladies dancing,
Ten pipers piping,
Nine drummers drumming,
Eight maids a-milking,
Seven swans a-swimming,
Six geese a-laying,
Five gold rings,
Four colly birds,
Three French hens,
Two turtle doves, and
A partridge in a pear tree.

Traditional

Miss Flora McFlimsey's Christmas Eve

by Mariana

Once there was an old doll whose name was Flora McFlimsey. She lived in a toy cupboard in the attic with a box of Tiddly-Winks and a Mother Goose book and Gulliver's Travels and a Noah's Ark and a fat sheep on wheels and an old, old, doll's trunk.

She had not always lived in the attic. No indeed! She had once belonged to the little girl with red-topped boots, who played with her in the nursery below. But the little girl had long ago grown up and married, and Miss Flora McFlimsey had been put away in the attic and forgotten.

There she sat next to the little trunk in a corner of the toy cupboard, wearing a faded silk dress and a straw hat with a blue ribbon on it.

She led a rather lonely life, of course, as there was no one to talk to except the fat sheep who could not even say Ba-a-a any more.

Indeed she would have been quite lonely except that she had one visitor, Timothy Mouse, who often looked in for a chat in the evenings after he'd made the rounds of the house.

Flora McFlimsey enjoyed Timothy Mouse's visits. He brought her news of the family downstairs, and what the children had for supper, and bits of gossip about the toys in the playroom.

One cold winter's night, when outside the snow was falling fast, Timothy Mouse appeared as usual through the little hole in the corner of the toy cupboard.

He always said "Hello" when he came in, but this evening he didn't say anything at all. He just wiggled his ears and blinked his eyes and ran three times around the floor of the cupboard after his tail.

Then he stopped and said in a low voice, "There are strange goings-on downstairs in the living room tonight, Miss McFlimsey. Stockings are hanging from the mantelpiece! And what is worse, a tree with shiny things all over it is growing right out of the floor."

"Ah," said Flora McFlimsey, sighing softly, "it must be Christmas Eve."

"What's that?" asked Timothy Mouse.

"Why that's the most wonderful night in the year," said Flora McFlimsey. "It's when Santa Claus comes down the chimney and puts presents in the children's stockings and under the Christmas tree, and people sing carols and . . ."

"Huh!" said Timothy Mouse, who did not like to think there was anything he didn't know, "it all sounds rather silly to me. I prefer birthdays with plenty of cake crumbs lying around. Well, I must be on my way," he added, and disappeared through the hole in the corner of the cupboard.

After he'd gone Miss Flora McFlimsey sat thinking about her first Christmas Eve.

She remembered how someone had taken her out of a long white box tied with satin ribbons and put her in a little red rocking chair under the Christmas tree. She remembered the blue velvet dress she had worn with a hat to match and a muff of ermine fur and a tiny gold locket and chain.

Early on Christmas morning a little girl in a fluffy white dress had come running in and cried, "Oh, isn't she beautiful!" and had hugged and kissed her.

But the velvet dress and the hat and the ermine muff and her little gold locket had disappeared long ago.

Things were different now. Maybe little girls didn't play with dolls any more. Timothy Mouse never said much about dolls in the playroom.

Miss Flora McFlimsey sighed. "I wish I could have just one little look at the Christmas tree," she said to herself.

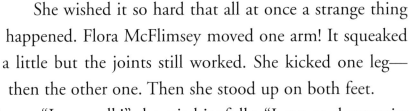

She wished it so hard that all at once a strange thing happened. Flora McFlimsey moved one arm! It squeaked a little but the joints still worked. She kicked one leg— then the other one. Then she stood up on both feet.

"I can walk!" she cried joyfully. "I can go downstairs and see the Christmas tree."

Four more steps and she was out of the toy cupboard. Then she walked straight to the top of the attic stairs.

Down these she climbed one by one, to the hall on the second floor. When she went past the door of the playroom where the children were sleeping, she tried to walk very softly and to keep her knees from squeaking.

Then she slid down the banisters of the front stairs and crossed the hall to the living room.

There was the tree all shining and beautiful, with an angel on the top, and in the firelight Miss Flora McFlimsey could see the stockings hanging in a row from the mantelpiece.

Everything was still as a mouse.

She crept over into the shadows and looked up at the Christmas tree.

"It is the most beautiful tree in all the world," she whispered, "and this is the most wonderful night in all the year."

Suddenly there was a little scratching sound in the chimney.

"Goodness! What was that?"

Miss Flora McFlimsey hid in the shadow of a big chair. There was more scratching, then the sound of feet stamping on the hearth-rug.

Flora McFlimsey peeped around the corner of the chair. There was Santa Claus taking a big pack off his back, and talking to himself.

"Dear, dear," he was saying, "I'm a doll short! Here's the bride doll for Suzy, and the doll with the red coat for Toto—but there's no doll for Diana! It must have dropped out when we dived  through the snow cloud. Dear, dear, dear! After all those letters she wrote me, too!"

He kept on saying "dear, dear" while he was stuffing presents into the stockings and piling them up under the Christmas tree.

All at once he caught sight of Miss Flora McFlimsey peeping out from behind the chair.

"Well, well, well," he said, "and who are you, please?"

Miss Flora McFlimsey trembled but she stepped out into the firelight and said in a tiny voice: "Good evening, sir. My name is Flora McFlimsey. I live in the attic and I came down to see the Christmas tree."

"Well, now, my dear," said Santa Claus. "It seems to me I've seen you before."

Santa Claus picked up Miss Flora

McFlimsey and looked hard at her. "Why, yes, I remember you very well. It was a long time ago, to be sure."

Then his frown disappeared and he smiled broadly. "Why, of course! You'll be just the doll for Diana." And he sat her down under the Christmas tree with the bride doll and the doll in the red coat.

"And now, my dear," he said, "I've a great deal more to do before morning, so good night to you all and a Merry Christmas!" And with that, he was up the chimney and away. There was a scurry of hoofs on the roof, then all was still again.

Miss Flora McFlimsey sat up straight and proud. She felt as if something wonderful were about to happen.

Then all at once Flora McFlimsey heard someone whispering. It was the tall doll in the red coat. "Did you see that scarecrow of an old doll over there?" she asked.

"Yes," answered the bride doll. "Isn't she a sight? Did you ever in all your life see such funny old-fashioned clothes? And that straw hat on Christmas Eve!" And they both laughed till they almost fell over.

"Just wait till the children see her! They'll send her right back to the

attic where she belongs," said the doll in the red coat.

All the happy feeling suddenly left Flora McFlimsey.

"It's true," she said to herself. "I'm old fashioned and my clothes are old fashioned. I had better go right back to the attic before the children see me." She tried to stand up. But all her joints had grown stiff again, and she could not even move an arm.

So there was nothing to do but to sit there till the children came in the morning and saw her. Tears came into Miss Flora McFlimsey's eyes and rolled down her cheeks.

If only Timothy Mouse had not told her it was Christmas Eve! She should never, never, never have left the toy cupboard in the attic.

Suddenly, from behind the fire-engine, a little dark shadow darted out and ran three times around in a circle. It was Timothy Mouse. He stopped close to Miss McFlimsey and wiggled his ears and whispered, "Cheer up! Help is coming soon."

Then he darted off into the shadows again.

Miss Flora McFlimsey straightened up.

What happened next could never be explained. Perhaps Timothy Mouse ran up the tree and whispered in the angel's ear, or perhaps the angel leaned over and saw Miss Flora McFlimsey and decided to come down and help.

And down she came, right to
Miss Flora McFlimsey's side and opened
the trunk which had appeared suddenly
under the Christmas tree. And there, on the
very top, was the little gold locket and chain
that Miss Flora McFlimsey had worn that first Christmas Eve. There,
too, were her blue velvet dress and her hat and her little ermine muff.

The angel helped Miss Flora McFlimsey take
off her faded, dusty dress and put on the blue
velvet one. She curled her hair and put the gold locket and
chain around her neck. Then she found a tiny lace handkerchief
in the trunk and a little bottle of eau de cologne.
She tucked these inside Miss Flora McFlimsey's ermine
muff and put a pair of white kid gloves on her little hands.
And one by one, the angel took the other things out of the trunk,
and hung them all on the low branches of the Christmas tree.

Then she leaned down and kissed Flora McFlimsey
on her round rosy cheek and whispered
something ever so softly in her ear.
It was something about Christmas and something about
love, but only Miss Flora McFlimsey heard her.

Then the angel said good night and climbed—no, she must have flown—back to her place on the top of the Christmas tree.

Miss Flora McFlimsey sat up very straight, holding her ermine muff in front of her. The doll in the red coat and the bride doll sat up very straight, too. They were all looking towards the door where the children would come in. It would soon be morning.

"They will like me best, I think," whispered the doll in the red coat. "I am dressed in the very latest style."

"I don't know about that," said the bride doll. "There is nothing so beautiful as a bride, you know."

Miss Flora McFlimsey said nothing but she trembled a little. At that moment she heard footsteps running down the stairs, and shouts of "Merry Christmas!"

In they came, Alex and Suzy and Billy and Diana and little round Toto.

They looked so happy that Miss Flora McFlimsey forgot to be afraid.

And then the wonderful thing that she had felt was about to happen, really did happen.

It was Diana who spied her first.

"Oh, look at the old doll," she cried. "Isn't she beautiful!"

"And look at all her dresses and things," cried Suzy.

"And her trunk," said Toto.

"I love her, I love her!" cried Diana. And she took Miss Flora McFlimsey in her arms.

"Let me hold her," cried Suzy. "And please let me dress her," cried Toto.

And the doll in the red coat? And the bride doll? Well, no one paid very much attention to them.

But Miss Flora McFlimsey was happy, for once again on a Christmas morning she had been hugged and kissed by a little girl!

We Are Not Alone

Captain's Log. Starship Saturnalian.
Earth year 2030, day 358—
The new drive worked! We've tracked the alien
spacecraft that vanished from earth's orbit late

last night. We followed its fantastic leap
across the galaxy and now can see
its sledge-like shape dropping in steep
descent to a planet. Incredibly

a single cosmonaut whose suit glows red
clings to its tail and holds long ropes to steer
a group of prancing creatures: from each head
sprout aerials that make them look like deer.

The planet's steaming, its surface smooth and
dark as Christmas pudding. Prepare to land!

Dave Calder

Bells

We went to a party
On Christmas Eve
And after tea
Mrs Turney said SSSSSSSHHHHHH
So we sssssssshed
And we heard them
The jingle of bells
The reindeer wear
Because they don't have hooters

Hiawyn Oram

Sir Winter

Christmas Weather

Good King Wenceslas

Good King Wenceslas looked out,
   On the feast of Stephen,
When the snow lay round about,
   Deep and crisp and even:
Brightly shone the moon that night,
   Though the frost was cruel,
When a poor man came in sight,
   Gathering winter fuel.

"Hither, page, and stand by me,
   If thou know'st it, telling,
Yonder peasant, who is he?
   Where and what his dwelling?"
"Sire, he lives a good league hence,
   Underneath the mountain,
Right against the forest fence,
   By Saint Agnes' fountain."

"Bring me flesh, and bring me wine,
   Bring me pine-logs hither;
Thou and I will see him dine,
   When we bear them thither."
Page and monarch, forth they went,
   Forth they went together;
Through the rude wind's wild lament
   And the bitter weather.

"Sire, the night is darker now,
    And the wind blows stronger;
Fails my heart, I know not how;
    I can go no longer."
"Mark my footsteps, good my page;
    Tread thou in them boldly:
Thou shalt find the winter's rage
    Freeze thy blood less coldly."

In his master's steps he trod,
    Where the snow lay dinted;
Heat was in the very sod
    Which the Saint had printed.
Therefore, Christian men, be sure,
    Wealth or rank possessing,
You who now will bless the poor,
    Shall yourselves find blessing.

J. M. Neale

Pilot

If I could be a pilot
Each Christmas Eve I'd fly
To fetch a fluffy snow cloud
From the distant Arctic sky,
I'd chase it, catch it, tow it home
And tie it to a tree,
So snow would fall on Christmas Day
On all my friends and me.

Richard Edwards

Sir Winter

I heard Sir Winter coming.
He crept out of his bed
and rubbed his thin and freezing hands:
"I'll soon be up!" he said.

"I'll shudder at the keyhole
and rattle at the door,
I'll strip the trees of all their leaves
and strew them on the floor.

"I'll harden every puddle
that Autumn thinks is his—
I'll lay a sparkling quilt of snow
on everything that is!

"I'll bring a load of darkness
as large as any coal,
and drive my husky dogs across
the world, from pole to pole.

"Oho! How you will shiver!"
—And then I heard him say;
"But in the middle of it all
I'll give you
                CHRISTMAS DAY!"

Jean Kenward

The Frozen Man

Out at the edge of town   a man is walking
where black trees   alone:

crack their fingers   on the coal-black road
in the icy wind   his cold

and hedges freeze   feet
on their shadows   ring

and the breath of cattle,   and
still as boulders,   ring.

hangs in rags
under the rolling moon,

Here in a snug house
at the heart of town

the fire is burning
red and yellow and gold:

you can hear the warmth
like a sleeping cat

breathe softly
in every room.

When the frozen man
comes to the door,

let him in,
let him in,
let him in.

Kit Wright

Snow

In the gloom of whiteness,
In the great silence of snow,
A child was sighing
And bitterly saying: "Oh,
They have killed a white bird up there on her nest,
The down is fluttering from her breast!"
And still it fell through the dusky brightness
On the child crying for the bird of the snow.

Edward Thomas

The Little Match Girl

by Hans Christian Andersen

Retold by Naomi Lewis

It was dreadfully cold. Snow was falling; soon it would be quite dark. It was also the very last evening of the year—New Year's Eve. In this cold and darkness, a poor little girl was wandering along, with bare head and bare feet. It's true that she had slippers on when she left home— but what good was that? They were great big things, those slippers; they had belonged to her mother, so it is not surprising that they had fallen off when she scurried across the road just missing two carts that were thundering past. One slipper was nowhere to be found, and a boy ran off with the other. It would do for a cradle when he had children of his own, he called out teasingly.

So there was the little girl treading along on naked feet that were quite blue with cold. In an old apron she carried a pile of matches, and she held one bunch of them in her hand. She had sold nothing the whole of the day; no one had given her a single penny. Hungry and frozen she trudged along looking so miserable. Poor little thing! The snowflakes fell on her long fair hair that curled so prettily at her neck. But she certainly wasn't thinking about her looks. Lights were shining in every window and wonderful smells of roasting goose drifted down the street. For it was New Year's Eve, remember, and that's what she was thinking about.

In a sheltered corner between two houses, one jutting out a little further than the other, she crouched down and huddled herself together, tucking up her legs—but this didn't help; she grew colder and colder. She didn't dare to go home, for she had sold no matches. She hadn't a single copper coin to bring back and so her father would beat her. Besides, her home was freezing too. It was an attic under the roof, and the wind whistled through that, though the worst cracks had been stuffed with straw and rags.

Her hands were quite numb with cold. A match flame would be such a comfort. Oh, if only she dared to strike one match, just one. She took one and struck it against the wall— crrritch! How it crackled and blazed! What a lovely warm clear flame, just like a little candle! She held her hand around it. Really, it was a wonderful light. The little girl seemed to be sitting in front of a big iron stove with shining brass knobs and fittings; inside was such a warm friendly fire. Oh, what had happened? She had just put out her toes to warm them too when—the flame went out. The stove had gone! She was sitting in the cold with the stump of a burnt-out matchstick in her hand.

She struck another match. It flared up brightly; where it shone, the wall became transparent as gauze. She could see right into the room where the table was laid with a shining starched white cloth; on it were dishes of finest porcelain. A delicious hot fragrance rose from a roast goose stuffed with prunes and apples. The goose seemed nearer and nearer—she could almost touch it. Then the match went out. All she could see and feel was the cold unfriendly wall.

She struck another. Now she was sitting under the loveliest of Christmas trees, even bigger and more beautifully decorated than the great tree she had seen at Christmas through the glass door of the rich merchant's shop. Thousands of candles were alight on its branches, and brightly coloured Christmas pictures, just like the ones in all the shop windows, were looking

down at her kindly. The little girl reached out her hands—then the match burned out. But the flames from the candles seemed to rise higher and higher, and she saw that they were the stars in the heavens, high above. One of them rushed across, leaving a fiery streak in the dark night sky.

"Someone is dying!" said the little girl. Her grandmother, now dead, the only person who had ever been kind to her, had told her once that whenever a star falls, it is a sign that a soul is going to God.

She struck another match on the wall. As it lit up the blackness all around, she saw in its bright glow her dear grandmother. How sweet she looked, so loving and so kind.

"Oh Granny, take me with you," she cried. "I know you'll disappear when the match goes out, just like the warm stove and the roast goose and the wonderful Christmas tree!" And without stopping she struck all the rest of the matches in the bundle. Her grandmother must not go!

The flames shone out so brilliantly that all around was even brighter than daylight. Never before had her grandmother looked so tall and beautiful. She took the little girl in her arms and flew with her in joy and splendour up and up to where there is no cold, no fear, no hunger—up to heaven.

In the cold early morning, huddled in a corner, there sat the little girl, with red cheeks and smiling lips—frozen to death on the last night of the old year. The New Year dawned on the little dead body with its lapful of matches; one bundle was burnt out. "She was trying to warm herself," people said. No one knew what lovely things she had seen, and how gloriously she had flown with her grandmother into her own New Year.

5 Ways to Stop Snowmen
Raiding the Fridge

1) Throw banana skins on the kitchen floor.

2) Hang hot-water bottles everywhere.

3) Fill the fridge with smelly socks.

4) Hire a bouncer.

5) Move to the Caribbean.

Roger McGough

Snow

Ben likes snow when it's first fallen
And there are only birds' feet in it
Em likes snow when it's deep
And she falls in it
And it fills her boots
I like snow when it's icy
And you can slide in it
And toboggan and ride in it
But when it turns to water
And it's just wet
Then we forget
How much we liked it when it was snow

Hiawyn Oram

In the Bleak Mid-Winter

In the bleak mid-winter
    Frosty wind made moan;
Earth stood hard as iron,
    Water like a stone;
Snow had fallen, snow on snow,
    Snow on snow,
In the bleak mid-winter,
    Long ago.

Our God, heaven cannot hold Him
    Nor earth sustain;
Heaven and earth shall flee away
    When He comes to reign;
In the bleak mid-winter
    A stable-place sufficed
The Lord God almighty,
    Jesus Christ.

Enough for Him, whom cherubim
   Worship night and day,
A breastful of milk,
   And a mangerful of hay;
Enough for Him, whom angels
   Fall down before,
The ox and ass and camel
   Which adore.

Angels and archangels
   May have gathered there,
Cherubim and seraphim
   Thronged the air;
But only His mother
   In her maiden bliss
Worshipped the Belovèd
   With a kiss.

What can I give Him,
   Poor as I am?
If I were a shepherd
   I would bring a lamb;
If I were a wise man
   I would do my part;
Yet what I can I give Him—
   Give my heart.

Christina Rossetti

Jingle Bells

Dashing through the snow,
In a one-horse open sleigh,
O'er the fields we go,
Laughing all the way;
Bells on bobtail ring,
Making spirits bright;
What fun it is to ride and sing
A sleighing song tonight.

Jingle bells, jingle bells,
Jingle all the way,
Oh, what fun it is to ride
In a one-horse open sleigh.

Jingle bells, jingle bells,
Jingle all the way,
Oh, what fun it is to ride
In a one-horse open sleigh.

Traditional

For Auld Lang Syne!

The New Year

The Fight of the Year

"And there goes the bell for the third month
and Winter comes out of its corner looking groggy
Spring leads with a left to the head
followed by a sharp right to the body

daffodils

primroses

crocuses

snowdrops

lilacs

violets

pussywillow

Winter can't take much more punishment
and Spring shows no signs of tiring

tadpoles

squirrels

baalambs

badgers

bunny rabbits

mad march hares

horses and hounds

Spring is merciless
Winter won't go the full twelve rounds

bobtail clouds

scallywaggy winds

the sun
a pavement artist
in every town
A left to the chin
and Winter's down!
1 tomatoes
2 radish
3 cucumber
4 onions
5 beetroot
6 celery
7 and any
8 amount
9 of lettuce
10 for dinner
Winter's out for the count
Spring is the winner!"

Roger McGough

Auld Lang Syne

Should auld acquaintance be forgot,
And never brought to min'?
Should auld acquaintance be forgot,
And auld lang syne?

For auld lang syne, my dear.
For auld lang syne,
We'll tak a cup o' kindness yet,
For auld lang syne.

We twa hae run about the braes,
And pu'd the gowans fine;
But we've wandered mony a weary foot
Sin' auld lang syne.
We twa hae paidled i' the burn,
From morning sun till dine;
But seas between us braid hae roared
Sin' auld lang syne.

And there's a hand, my trusty fiere,
And gie's a hand o' thine;
And we'll tak a right guid-willie waught,
For auld lang syne.

And surely ye'll be your pint-stowp,
And surely I'll be mine;
And we'll tak a cup o' kindness yet
For auld lang syne.

For auld lang syne, my dear.
For auld lang syne,
We'll tak a cup o' kindness yet,
For auld lang syne.

Robert Burns

Thoughts for a Cold Day

A little bit of blowing,
　A little bit of snow,
A little bit of growing,
　And crocuses will show;
On every twig that's lonely
　A new green leaf will spring;
On every patient tree-top
　A thrush will stop and sing.

Anon.

Index of Titles

Index of Authors and Poets

Acknowledgements

The publishers wish to thank the following for permission to use copyright material:

Robert Barry, *Mr Willowby's Christmas Tree*, by permission of Random House, Inc. **Gerard Benson**, 'Lullaby Carol' written for a nativity play at Starcross Infants School, Islington, by permission of the author. **Clare Bevan**, 'The Lamb's Story' and 'Just Doing My Job' by permission of the author. **Michael Bond**, 'Paddington's Christmas' from *More About Paddington* by permission of The Agency (London) Ltd and Houghton Mifflin Company. Text copyright © Michael Bond 1959. First published in Great Britain in 1959 by William Collins Sons & Co Ltd. All rights reserved and enquiries to The Agency (London) Ltd. **Thomas Boyle**, 'Christmas to Me Was Snow' by permission of *The Daily Mirror*. **Dave Calder**, 'We Are Not Alone' by permission of the author. **Charles Causley**, 'They're Fetching in Ivy and Holly' from *Collected Poems for Children*, Macmillan Children's Books, and 'High in the Heaven' from *The Gift of a Lamb*, Robson Books, by permission of David Higham Associates. **Hans Christian Andersen**, 'The Little Match Girl' from *The Flying Trunk and Other Stories* retold by Naomi Lewis, Beaver Books, by permission of Andersen Press. **Dorothy Edwards**, 'The Naughtiest Story of All' from *My Naughty Little Sister*, Methuen Children's Books, a division of Egmont Children's Books Limited, by permission of Egmont Children's Books Ltd. **Richard Edwards**, 'Pilot' from *If Only* copyright © Richard Edwards, 1990 by permission of Felicity Bryan and the author. **U. A. Fanthorpe**, 'What The Donkey Saw' and 'Reindeer Report' from *Poems for Christmas*, Harry Chambers/Peterloo Poets, by permission of Peterloo Poets. **Eleanor Farjeon**, 'Keeping Christmas' from *Silver Sand and Snow* published by Michael Joseph by permission of David Higham Associates. **Aileen Fisher**, 'Christmas Secrets' from *Out in the Dark and Daylight*, copyright © 1980 Aileen Fisher, by permission of Marian Reiner on behalf of the author. **Kenneth Grahame**, 'Mole's Christmas' from *The Wind in the Willows* copyright The University Chest, Oxford, by permission of Curtis Brown, London. **James Herriot**, *The Christmas Day Kitten*, Michael Joseph Ltd, by permission of David Higham Associates. **Russell Hoban**, 'Small, Smaller' from *The Pedalling Man*, Heinemann, by permission of David Higham Associates. **Jean Kenward**, 'Sir Winter' by permission of the author. **Astrid Lindgren**, extract from *Pippi Longstocking in the South Seas (Pippi Langstrump Isöderhavet)* by permission of Oxford University Press and Saltkråkan AB. **Mariana**, *Miss Flora McFlimsey's Christmas Eve*, copyright © 1949 by Lothrop, Lee & Shepard Co, Inc, by permission of William Morrow & Company, Inc. **Roger McGough**, 'The Fight of the Year' from *Watchwords*, Cape, and '5 Ways to Stop Snowmen Raiding the Fridge' from *Bad Bad Cats*, Viking Penguin, by permission of The Peters Fraser and Dunlop Group Limited on behalf of Roger McGough. **A. A. Milne**, 'King John's Christmas' from *Now We Are Six* © A. A. Milne. Copyright under the Berne Convention. Published by Methuen, an imprint of Egmont Children's Books Limited, London and used with permission. **Adrian Mitchell**, 'Mrs Christmas' from *All My Own Stuff*, Simon & Schuster, by permission of The Peters Fraser and Dunlop Group Limited on behalf of Adrian Mitchell. Educational Health Warning! Adrian Mitchell asks that none of his poems are used in connection with any examinations whatsoever. **Tony Mitton**, 'Santa's Sad Sack' from *While Shepherds Washed Their Socks* and 'Mince Pie Chant' by permission of the author. **Hiawyn Oram**, 'Bells' and 'Snow' from *Speaking for Ourselves*, Methuen, copyright © 1990 Hiawyn Oram, by permission of Rogers, Coleridge & White Ltd, London, on behalf of the author. **Christopher Pilling**, 'The Meeting Place' from *Poems for Christmas*, Harry Chambers/Peterloo Poets, by permission of Peterloo Poets. **Clive Sansom**, 'Santa Claus' from *The Golden Unicorn*, Methuen, by permission of David Higham Associates. **Dylan Thomas**, extract from 'Memories of Christmas' from *Quite Early One Morning*, J. M. Dent. Published in the USA as *The Collected Stories of Dylan Thomas*, copyright © 1954 by New Directions Publishing Corp. Reprinted by permission of New Directions Publishing Corp and David Higham Associates. **Robert Westall**, *The Witness*, Macmillan Children's Books and Dutton Children's Books. Text copyright © 1986 by Robert Westall, by permission of Macmillan Children's Books, London and Dutton Children's Books, a division of Penguin Putnam, Inc. **Charles Williams**, 'Kings Came Riding' from *Modern Verse for Little Children*, Oxford University Press, by permission of David Higham Associates. **Kit Wright**, 'The Frozen Man' from *Rabbiting On*, HarperCollins Publishers, by permission of the author.

Every effort has been made to trace the copyright holders but if any have been inadvertently overlooked the publishers will be pleased to make the necessary arrangement at the first opportunity.